Contents

Biopsychosocial Aspects of Bereavement

Edited by
Sidney Zisook, M.D.

1400 K Street, N.W.
Washington, DC 20005

Note: The authors have worked to ensure that all information in this book concerning drug dosages, schedules, and routes of administration is accurate as of the time of publication and consistent with standards set by the U.S. Food and Drug Administration and the general medical community. As medical research and practice advance, however, therapeutic standards may change. For this reason and because human and mechanical errors sometimes occur, we recommend that readers follow the advice of a physician who is directly involved in their care or the care of a member of their family.

Manufactured in the United States of America

The paper used in this publication meets the minimum requirements of American National Standard for Information Sciences—Permanence of Paper for Printed Library Materials, ANSI Z39.48-1984.

Library of Congress Cataloging-in-Publication Data

Biopsychosocial aspects of bereavement.

(The Progress in psychiatry series)
Includes bibliographies.
1. Bereavement—Psychological aspects.
2. Grief. 3. Adjustment (Psychology)
4. Neuropsychiatry. I. Zisook, Sidney, 1934-
II. Series. [DNLM: 1. Adaptation, Psychological. 2. Grief.
3. Neurobiology. 4. Social Adjustment. BF 575.G7 B63]
RC455.4.L67B56 1987 155.9'37 86-28865
ISBN 0-88048-135-8 (alk. paper)

Contributors

Richard DeVaul, M.D.
Professor and Dean, West Virginia University Medical School, Morgantown, West Virginia

Thomas R. Faschingbauer, Ph.D.
Associate Clinical Professor, Department of Psychiatry/Medical School, University of Texas at Houston, Houston, Texas

Morris Green, M.D.
Professor and Chairman, Department of Pediatrics, Indiana University School of Medicine, Indianapolis, Indiana

Michael Irwin, M.D.
Assistant Professor, Department of Psychiatry, University of California, San Diego, La Jolla, California

Selby C. Jacobs, M.D.
Associate Professor, Yale University Department of Psychiatry, New Haven, Connecticut

Lucy E. Lyons
Research Associate, University of California, San Diego, UCSD-Gifford Mental Health Center, San Diego, California

Marian Osterweis, Ph.D.
Senior Professional Associate, Division of Mental Health and Behavioral Medicine, Institute of Medicine, National Academy of Sciences, Washington, D.C.

Edward K. Rynearson, M.D.
Clinical Associate Professor of Psychiatry, University of Washington, The Mason Clinic, Seattle, Washington

Stephen B. Shanfield, M.D.
Professor of Psychiatry, University of Texas Health Science Center, San Antonio, Texas

Stephen R. Shuchter, M.D.
Associate Clinical Professor, University of California, San Diego, UCSD-Gifford Mental Health Center, San Diego, California

Fredric Solomon, M.D.
Director, Division of Mental Health and Behavioral Medicine, Institute of Medicine, National Academy of Sciences, Washington, D.C.

Herbert Weiner, M.D.
Professor, Department of Psychiatry and Biobehavioral Sciences, University of California, Los Angeles, Los Angeles, California

Sidney Zisook, M.D.
Associate Professor, University of California, San Diego, UCSD-Gifford Mental Health Center, San Diego, California

Introduction to the Progress in Psychiatry Series

The *Progress in Psychiatry* Series is designed to capture in print the excitement that comes from assembling a diverse group of experts from various locations to examine in detail the newest information about a developing aspect of psychiatry. This series emerged as a collaboration between the American Psychiatric Association's Scientific Program Committee and the American Psychiatric Press, Inc. Great interest was generated by a number of the symposia presented each year at the APA Annual Meeting, and we realized that much of the information presented there, carefully assembled by people who are deeply immersed in a given area, would unfortunately not appear together in print. The symposia sessions at the Annual Meetings provide an unusual opportunity for experts who otherwise might not meet on the same platform to share their diverse viewpoints for a period of three hours. Some new themes are repeatedly reinforced and gain credence, while in other instances disagreements emerge, enabling the audience and now the reader to reach informed decisions about new directions in the field. The *Progress in Psychiatry* Series allows us to publish and capture some of the best of the symposia and thus provide an in-depth treatment of specific areas which might not otherwise be presented in broader review formats.

Psychiatry is by nature an interface discipline, combining the study of mind and brain, of individual and social environments, of the humane and the scientific. Therefore, progress in the field is rarely linear—it often comes from unexpected sources. Further, new developments emerge from an array of viewpoints that do not necessarily provide immediate agreement but rather expert examination of the issues. We intend to present innovative ideas and data that will enable you, the reader, to participate in this process.

We believe the *Progress in Psychiatry* Series will provide you with an opportunity to review timely new information in specific fields of interest as they are developing. We hope you find that the excitement of the presentations is captured in the written word and that this book proves to be informative and enjoyable reading.

David Spiegel, M.D.
Series Editor
Progress in Psychiatry Series

Introduction

Grieving the death of a close friend or relative is an almost universal, potentially devastating experience that at some time or other affects us all. It is a prototypical life stress event which most often is associated with acute turmoil and distress, and, at times, may lead to substantial psychological and/or medical morbidity, possibly even to death. The boundaries between normal or uncomplicated grief and pathological mourning are not always clear. The distinction, however, is clinically significant, as "normal" grief is generally considered self-limited, relatively benign, and not amenable to therapeutic intervention; whereas pathological grief may be associated with enormous social, psychological, behavioral, and medical morbidity, and may warrant intensive intervention. The reasons for any individual crossing the boundary from "uncomplicated" to pathological mourning are myriad and may include sociological (poverty, role demands, support systems), psychological (dependency, ambivalence), or biological (health, genetic predispositions) factors.

The chapters in this book, in one way or another, all deal with these boundary issues. First, Chapter 1 presents an overview of the grieving process that conceptualizes bereavement as a disruptive life-stress event with far-reaching biopsychosocial consequences. In this opening chapter, normative reactions for both children and adults are emphasized. The second chapter, on the other hand, covers pathological forms of mourning by focusing on the effects of unresolved grief.

Chapters 3 through 5 deal primarily with psychosocial aspects of bereavement, addressing both natural and unnatural causes of death. Chapters 3 and 4 focus on a form of grief that is often considered the most disruptive of all life events, spousal bereavement. First, Chapter 3 presents a multidimensional model for assessing and understanding the adjustment to widowhood. Using this model, Chapter 4 examines the natural history and course of spousal bereavement over a four-year period. Chapter 5 focuses on reactions to unnatural causes of death such as suicide, homicide, and accidents.

Chapters 6 through 8 deal with predicting and measuring outcome. Chapter 6 examines predictors of good and poor outcome in bereavement. Chapters 7 and 8 deal with the all important questions of how to measure and/or operationalize grief. The development of one of the few paper and pencil measures of grief, The Texas Revised Inventory of Grief, is discussed in Chapter 7. Chapter 8 reviews the literature on currently available measures of grief and bereavement.

Biological aspects of bereavement are explored in Chapters 9 and 10. The studies that are described and discussed here cover the effects of loss on two highly integrative bodily systems considered to be important mediators between a variety of life stressors and illness: the neuroendocrine (Chapter 9) and the immune systems (Chapter 10). The final chapter, utilizing the biological, psychological, and sociological parameters of bereavement examined in the first 10 chapters, describes a multidimensional approach to counseling and treating bereaved individuals.

If there is an overriding theme to this book, it is that grief affects all aspects of the survivor's being. Not only does a bereaved individual have to contend with sadness and mourning, but also with biological alterations, changes in other relationships and roles, financial exigencies, and a host of additional challenges. The process of grief can be either growth-promoting or destructive, and often it is both. Grief is a phenomenon about which much is known, but given its prevalence and potentially deleterious consequences, much more needs to be learned. We hope this book adds to the current data base and encourages an appreciation of the significance of a comprehensive, integrative, biopsychosocial approach to grief and bereavement.

Sidney Zisook, M.D.

Chapter 1

Bereavement Reactions, Consequences, and Care

Marian Osterweis, Ph.D.
Fredric Solomon, M.D.
Morris Green, M.D.

Chapter 1

Bereavement Reactions, Consequences, and Care

Bereavement is usually considered to have the most powerful impact of all events of ordinary life. It typically results not only in grief and emotional distress but also in perturbations in physiologic functioning and social disorganization. To be bereaved has been likened to being an immigrant in a foreign country—social relationships are altered, expectations for behavior are unclear, and one is generally disoriented. As with many other stressors, the consequences of bereavement are not uniform; many factors can modify that stress and affect long-term outcomes. The sudden and unexpected suicide of a young husband and father, for example, is likely to have much more profound effects on surviving family members than the long anticipated death of an elderly grandparent after a protracted illness.

Although clearly not unique in all respects, some aspects of loss through death are distinctive. Even superb coping abilities cannot alter the finality of death. The survivors' helplessness and total inability to control the event of death may account for the particularly stressful nature of this nearly universal experience.

Given that each year an estimated eight million Americans experience the death of an immediate family member and countless others experience other significant deaths, bereavement is a risk factor for a potentially major public health problem. Indeed, it was this concern that stimulated the Office of Prevention of the National Institute of Mental Health to request that the Institute of Medicine of the National Academy of Sciences[1] (see notes at end of references) study the factors that affect the bereavement process and its impact on general health and mental health. The study was mandated to address the following questions:

- What can be concluded from available research evidence about the health consequences of bereavement?

- Based on both research evidence and informed judgment, are there preventive interventions that should be recommended for more widespread adoption in the health care system?
- What further research would be especially important and promising to pursue?

The committee that conducted this study from 1982 to 1984 included clinicians and researchers from a wide range of disciplines, including psychiatry, psychology, social work, nursing, medicine (internal medicine, family practice, and pediatrics), the neurosciences, epidemiology, sociology, anthropology, and the ministry.[2] This chapter draws on the major findings of the Institute of Medicine committee's report (1).

THE PHASES OF BEREAVEMENT REACTIONS IN ADULTS

The first systematic study of bereavement was conducted by Erich Lindemann in 1944 (2). He described uncomplicated grief as a syndrome with a predictable course and distinctive symptoms, including: a) somatic distress (physical symptoms); b) preoccupation with the image of the deceased; c) guilt; d) hostility; e) loss of usual patterns of conduct; and, in some people, f) appearance of traits of the deceased (such as mannerisms or symptoms associated with a prior illness). Since the time of that study, numerous clinicians and researchers have sought to corroborate these observations and to describe the grieving process in adults.

The most immediate response following death, even when the loss has been anticipated, is shock, numbness, and a sense of disbelief. Because the reality of death has not yet penetrated awareness, survivors can appear to others to be holding up well and as though they are quite accepting of the loss. This numbness usually turns to intense feelings of separation and pain in the days and weeks after the funeral.

> The absence of the dead person is everywhere palpable. The home and familiar environs seem full of painful reminders. Grief breaks over the bereaved in waves of distress. There is intense yearning, pining, and longing for the one who has died. The bereaved feels empty inside, as though torn apart or as if the dead person had been torn out of his body (3).

During this phase the bereaved frequently report illusions and misperceptions, such as "seeing" the dead person in the street and having dreams in which the deceased is still alive. Eventually, these "searching" behaviors begin to decrease, and when the lost person fails to return, despair sets in. Depressed moods, difficulty in concentrating, anger at the deceased for dying, guilt about what else might have been done to avoid death, irritability, anxiety, restlessness, and extreme sadness are common reactions during this time. Even the best-meaning offers of comfort and support are often rejected because the grieving person is so focused on the deceased.

Also typical of the early aftermath of bereavement are dramatic and rapid swings from one feeling state to another. Avoidance of reminders of the deceased may alternate with deliberate cultivation of memories for some period of time. Gradually the death begins to become accepted. However, the bereaved may be intellectually aware of the finality of the loss long before their emotions allow full acceptance of the information as true. Depression and emotional swings are characteristic of most people for at least several months and often for more than a year following bereavement.

When does the bereavement process end? What are the signs that a favorable outcome has been achieved? There are no clear-cut answers to these questions. Terms such as "recovery," "adaptation," and "completion" have been used to describe the end of the bereavement process. Each term has somewhat different connotations and contributes to understanding, but no single term provides an adequate description.

A healthy bereavement process can be expected to include recovery of lost functions—including interest in current life, hopefulness, and the capacity to experience gratification, adaptation to new roles and statuses, and completion of acute grieving. Both favorable and unfavorable outcomes along several dimensions can be identified.

One of the most important dimensions is time. Despite the popular belief that the bereavement process is normally completed in a year, data from systematic studies and from clinical reports confirm that the process may be considerably more attenuated for many people and still fall well within normal boundaries. It is not the length of time per se that distinguishes normal from abnormal grief, but the quality and quantity of reactions over time. Thus, a precise endpoint in time cannot be specified.

Just as individuals vary in their reactions to grief, so too is there variation in terms of outcome. What may signal a healthy recovery for one individual may be a sign of continuing difficulty for another. For example, readiness to invest in new relationships does not invariably indicate completion of or recovery from grief. A seemingly quick remarriage or a decision to have another child after one has died may reflect a sense of hope or strength in one case, whereas in another case such actions may stem mainly from a wish to avoid grief.

For some, bereavement provides an opportunity for personal growth that might not otherwise have occurred. Among widows who had very traditional marriages, for example, the death of a husband may force them to take on new roles and acquire new skills. Being able to rise to these challenges successfully may leave a widow with a greater sense of competence and independence than she had when she married (4). Some have speculated that bereavement may lead to heightened creativity, noting that numerous successful artists, writers, and musicians have experienced painful losses.

CHILDREN'S BEREAVEMENT REACTIONS

Although they share some similarities with adults, children's reactions to loss often do not look like adults' reactions. Many differences in behavior, as well as the special vulnerability of children, are due to immaturity and lack of well developed coping mechanisms. For example, a child who plays games of death or funerals, one who tells strangers on the street "my sister died," or one who resumes play as if nothing distressing has happened, is not behaving inappropriately. Rather, the child is trying to master the loss, test others' reactions to the event, or protect himself from emotions so strong that they can be endured only for brief periods. Feelings that are expressed through misbehavior or angry outbursts may not appear to be, but often are, grief related. Furthermore, children are likely to exhibit these behaviors for many years after the loss has occurred.

Children's ability to work through bereavement, to complete their mourning, depends in part on their ability to distinguish between death and more temporary separations. In the past, some experts asserted that because very young children do not understand death and lack the capacity to mourn in a manner analogous to adults, they are therefore unable to complete the process and are likely to have problems for the rest of their lives. A substantial body of research literature now demonstrates that even very young children are able to grieve and make use of family supports to cope with loss. The chief difference between bereft children and adults is in the way in which children manifest their grief, and their need to rework and reintegrate understanding of the loss as they are then able to comprehend the event at new levels (1).

Immediately following bereavement, young children are likely to feel sad, angry, and fearful. Depending on their age they may have eating, bowel and bladder, or speech disturbances, and also commonly develop sleep disturbances. They may become withdrawn or excessively caregiving. School behavior and academic achievement may deteriorate and remain poor for several years after the death of a parent (5). Some children fear that they caused the death; they worry that they too might die, that the dead parent or sibling will return to seek revenge, or that the surviving caretaker will die and they will be abandoned. Children may see themselves as helpless and vulnerable, or as hostile and destructive, and use primitive defense mechanisms such as denial, aggression, and idealization in coping with their loss (6).

While adolescents are thought to have the maturity to experience sustained pain and complete their mourning, they too have a special vulnerability because they are simultaneously experiencing the normal developmental turbulence of adolescence and ambivalent feelings toward their parents. This already confusing time in life can only be made more disturbing if the adolescent must deal with the death of a parent, sibling, or peer through illness, or the shock of a violent death by suicide or accident.

HEALTH CONSEQUENCES OF BEREAVEMENT

The evidence from clinical experience and several kinds of research—epidemiologic, case follow-up, clinical, and social science—leads to several important conclusions. First, bereavement is associated with measurable distress in virtually everyone. Second, the distress, which can vary greatly in intensity and in the extent of interference with function, is long lasting. A survivor's way of life can be altered for as long as three years and commonly is disturbed for at least one year. Third, there is tremendous variation in individuals' reactions to bereavement. These reactions consist of a number of intertwined processes—psychologic, social, and biologic. They cannot be neatly plotted in a series of well-defined stages, nor is movement from the impact of the death to the resolution of bereavement likely to be in a straight path. Individuals will vary in terms of speed of recovery and in the amount of back-and-forth movement between phases. And even after the bereavement process is "completed," new waves of sadness may be triggered by important family events or other significant occasions. Such "anniversary reactions" may never entirely disappear. Fourth, as has been recorded in myth and literature over the centuries, and as suggested by individual clinical experience, some bereaved persons are at increased risk for illness and even death. Although early retrospective studies conducted from vital statistics (7) concluded that morbidity and mortality following bereavement were extremely likely, more recent carefully controlled prospective studies (8) reveal that such risks are not uniformly distributed.

It appears that:

- Following conjugal bereavement, young and middle-aged widowers are about 1½ times more likely to die prematurely than their married counterparts. Although greatest during the first year, this increased risk of mortality continues for many years unless the men remarry (8).
- For women, there is some evidence suggesting increased mortality in the second year, but not the first one, following bereavement (9).
- Higher mortality rates in men are due to increases in the relative risk of death by suicide, accidents, cardiovascular disease, and some infectious diseases.
- In widows, the relative risk of death from cirrhosis and, perhaps, suicide increases.
- Increased alcohol consumption, smoking, and use of tranquilizers and other medicines are well documented among the bereaved, especially among people who used these substances prior to the loss. Thus, bereavement appears to exacerbate and precipitate health-compromising behaviors.
- Psychologic and somatic depressive symptoms are characteristic following bereavement. For most people these symptoms abate after a few months. However, it has commonly been observed that a year or more after their loss 10 to 20 percent of the widowed still have a constellation of symptoms constituting a depressive syndrome (10). This means that out of the approximately 800,000 people who are widowed each year, 80,000 to 160,000 people may suffer subsequently from serious depression. The number of depressed or otherwise mentally disturbed individuals following other types of bereavement—death of a child, sibling, or parent—is not known.
- Bereavement may exacerbate existing illnesses, precipitate depression leading to suicide, aggravate or lead to alcohol abuse that can result in cirrhosis of the liver, and leave people vulnerable to infectious diseases.

Because of their psychosocial, emotional, and cognitive immaturity, it is generally agreed that bereaved children are especially vulnerable to psychopathology and that the full impact of bereavement may not be realized until many years later (3). Enduring psychologic symptoms of neurosis and depression have been observed in community and patient samples of children who have lost a parent or sibling (5). Several studies report a relationship between childhood bereavement and later mental illness, especially depression (6), in adult life, as well as increased risk of suicide. Although some bereaved children surely are at increased risk for a number of adverse consequences, current data do not support the impression that the negative results are as widespread or as inevitable as formerly thought. Many factors subsequent to the death—including the normal developmental push and the adequacy of caretakers—affect ultimate outcome (1).

For adults and children the nature of the distress and its manifestations depend on a host of biological, psychological, social, and situational factors that place individuals at risk or protect them from adversity. Although rigorous studies of these many risk factors have not been conducted, there are several that appear to be good predictors of certain outcomes of bereavement. Poor previous physical health is associated with poor physical health following bereavement. Mental illness, especially depression, is likewise likely to be exacerbated following bereavement and to interfere with normal grieving (11). Perceived social support is the best replicated predictor of psychosocial adjustment (12, 13). However, it is not clear whether the mere presence of social support leads to good outcomes, or whether people who were emotionally healthy to begin with are able to elicit social support to meet their needs following bereavement. For children who have lost a parent or sibling, the presence of a consistent, dependable caretaker seems to be especially important in determining outcome.

BIOLOGIC PERSPECTIVES

The functioning of all major bodily systems is likely to be altered during times of stress, including grief. Changes in the endocrine, immune, autonomic nervous, and cardiovascular systems have been observed, as well as disturbances of chronobiological organization. All of these systems are fundamentally influenced by brain function and neurotransmitters. Although changes in functioning have been documented by many researchers, the significance of these changes is not well understood. These physiological perturbations clearly represent reactions to a stressor—in this case, bereavement (14). However, just as psychosocial reactions may or may not presage mental disorder, physiologic reactions may or may not lead to documentable consequences. It is likely that they are adaptive physiologic responses that in some people may become maladaptive and eventually deleterious to health if they continue for too long or if they become too extreme. The notion that a normal physiologic adaptation to grief can become unregulated and lead to illness is consistent with the evidence for some autoimmune diseases (for example, chronic active hepatitis) (1).

Many studies have tried to establish a link between grief and specific diseases such as various forms of cancer, heart disease, and ulcers (15, 16). The evidence for such causal connections is generally very weak. The best current thinking is that it is unlikely that it will be found that grief is a specific stressor that causes a particular disease. It is more likely that the stress of bereavement triggers multiple changes which, in people who are vulnerable because of genetic predisposition or past or current illness, might lead to disease.

Quite apart from actual disease, recently bereaved people frequently report a host of physical complaints. They include pain, gastrointestinal disturbances, sleep and appetite disturbances, lack of energy, and other very "vegetative" symptoms that at another time might signal the presence of depression. Especially in the elderly, this grief-related depression may be misdiagnosed as organic dysfunction if health professionals are not aware of the nature of bereavement reactions and the history of the particular patient.

INTERVENING TO ASSIST THE BEREAVED

Viewed in its broadest sense, the term "preventive intervention" includes education, assessment, and primary, secondary, and tertiary prevention. From that perspective, there are a number of informal and formal activities that might usefully be undertaken with the bereaved in the community and as a part of humane and professionally responsible health care.

The evidence suggests that everyone needs support, reassurance, and some education and information following bereavement. This may be provided by families, friends, or clergy in an informal way, by laypeople in similar circumstances, through a community support group, or by health professionals.

Public Education

That the public wants information about bereavement is evidenced by the amount of attention paid to this topic in the mass media and by the growth of lay and professional literature directed to the public. In recent years there have been numerous articles, television shows, and radio programs dealing with people's reactions to bereavement. Although there are no studies to document the effects of information on the bereavement process, there is a widespread view that thorough information of several types can be beneficial and often seems to be lacking.

People need information to prepare themselves for the death of someone close and to respond sensitively to others in similar situations. This has been a major activity of many mutual support groups. Because bereavement is and should be handled largely by families and other informal social networks, public education about reactions to bereavement and how they might differ for adults and children, and for mothers and fathers, should be encouraged so that families and friends can provide the best possible support for the bereaved. Knowledge of bereavement reactions may be particularly important for those who interact routinely with children. Parents, teachers, and pediatricians should be able to recognize the signs that indicate a need for professional mental health intervention, including those that may not arise until long after their bereavement.

Mutual Support Interventions

Not all bereaved people need or want formal intervention, though mutual support groups may fill a gap for those who have little other social support. There is some evidence to suggest that intervention programs help people to move faster through the grieving process. Shortening a normal process that is painful for an individual and for those around him, even if it is not likely to result in long term dysfunction, may be of considerable intrinsic value.

Because of the paucity of outcome data regarding the efficacy of interventions, it is not entirely clear which programs are appropriate for whom and when. However, the Institute of Medicine committee (1) offered some guidance about the appropriateness of the general approaches under various circumstances.

Experience from the widow-to-widow programs suggests that immediately following bereavement people are not generally ready to seek help outside their immediate social network or to benefit from it; for at least several weeks they are likely to feel more or less numb and to have the support of family and friends (4). There is some evidence suggesting that a formal program during the very early period of crisis can be helpful for persons who are at high risk (17), or for mothers who lose newborns (18), but that for the general population of bereaved individuals, such an immediate intervention will have little impact.

Experiences from mutual support groups and hospices suggest that after several weeks, one-to-one support from someone who has experienced bereavement may be useful. The opportunity to talk with another widow, for example, who has had the same experience, can offer practical advice, and can assure the newly bereaved person that things will seem better soon is often very reassuring. Not until several months after bereavement do most widows feel ready to join a support group of other widows (19).

For people who experience normal reactions and who are not seen as being at particularly high risk for adverse consequences of bereavement, the support of family and friends, perhaps augmented by some type of mutual support intervention, will generally be sufficient.

Responsibilities of Health Care Professionals

It is being increasingly recognized that the well-being of the family and others close to a dying patient is part of health professionals' responsibility in terminal illness, and that the health care professionals and institutions have a continuing responsibility to assist the bereaved. This is not to suggest that health professionals must routinely engage in long-term counseling of the bereaved. It does suggest, however, that within the context of ongoing medical care, professionals have some responsibility—beyond simple human compassion—to become knowledgeable about bereavement and skilled in dealing with it. The education of health care professionals should prepare them to provide information, offer emotional support, recognize the red flags that may signal a need for professional mental health intervention, and be knowledgeable about both lay and professional community resources to which the bereaved can be referred as appropriate and desired.

The Institute of Medicine committee (1) felt strongly that these somewhat specialized skills must rest on the broader foundations that health and mental health education (and pastoral counseling) provide in order to be effective. It did not endorse the development and certification of a new profession for "grief counseling" that is separate from existing health and social services.

Need for professional mental health intervention. It is readily apparent that most bereaved individuals do not need professional mental health treatment. Yet there are certain symptoms and circumstances of bereavement for people in all cultural groups that should trigger a referral and are likely to warrant professional intervention. For both adults and children, a prior history of mental illness, especially depression, and the suicide of someone close, are likely to render them especially vulnerable and therefore candidates for close professional monitoring following bereavement. Persistent somatic complaints or depressive symptoms that do not lessen in intensity over time may also be signs of difficulty. In children, repeated aggressive or hostile behavior toward others, a prolonged drop in school performance, or regressive and insecure behaviors that persist over time are additional signs that help may be needed. For adults, drug and alcohol abuse, other health-injurious behaviors, a difficulty in maintaining social relationships, and an individual's own perception that he or she is not doing well, should trigger a professional referral for evaluation. Furthermore, if the production of an individual's symptoms is associated with family dysfunction, it is logical to include a family assessment and treatment when dealing with abnormal bereavement states.

A caution about prescribing drugs for bereavement reactions. A number of drugs are rather commonly prescribed to help ease the pain of bereavement. Clinical reports indicate that sedatives and minor tranquilizers are prescribed for a substantial proportion of bereaved individuals primarily for insomnia, and tricyclic antidepressants are prescribed for some people. However, many physicians have been hesitant to prescribe medication, particularly antidepressants, for patients experiencing grief reactions, even when these are intense, distressing, and disabling. The view is widely held that to suppress the grief experience will have later adverse consequences (2, 20). Yet no controlled trials have been reported in the literature to assess the long-term or short-term, positive or negative effects of any of these drugs upon grief. In the absence of such data, clinicians should exercise caution in prescribing medications for bereaved individuals and should inform patients of the potentially grave effects of combining alcohol with these drugs.

RESEARCH OPPORTUNITIES

Despite a large body of literature there are serious gaps in current understanding about the bereavement process, its outcomes, and the methods to assist the bereaved. Inadequacies in the data bases (such as the narrow scope of research, lack of good multidisciplinary studies, and some pervasive methodological problems) have hampered the development of definitive conclusions.

Research on the Processes and Outcomes of Bereavement

High priority should be given to research aimed at better documentation and refinement of those factors that place particular individuals or groups at high risk following the death of someone close. Current hypotheses about the subpopulations that are at risk for particular adverse consequences should be tested and prospective studies should be designed to identify characteristics of new subgroups. More definitive knowledge about individual risk factors and their interplay holds the promise of identification of high-risk individuals and the design of interventions to prevent or mitigate specific negative outcomes.

To accomplish this goal, the scope of research must be broadened. Although there is a vast literature from many different disciplines, most of it is on conjugal bereavement in adults and parental bereavement in children. There is very little data on the nature and consequences of bereavement following the death of a sibling at any age, of a child at any age, or of parents during adult life. Research on specific losses would clarify understanding of the special problems of each. Current understanding of the relationship between bereavement and the nature of the death is also very limited; the traumatic impact of violent death, for example, may alter the survivor's grieving process in highly significant ways.

Second, the health consequences of bereavement, especially the medical ones, are less well researched for children than for adults who have lost a spouse. Most studies of children are retrospective and have not used control groups. Most are based on responses of children who are receiving mental health care or, in the case of very young children, are based on observation of institutionalized children. Controlled studies of community samples of bereaved children should be conducted. Professionals' current knowledge does not clearly indicate whether it is bereavement itself or the way a child is dealt with and cared for subsequently that has the greatest effect on long-term outcome. Prospective longitudinal studies that follow children for many years could shed some light on this issue.

Third, most of what is known about bereavement comes from observations made in the United States, the United Kingdom, Australia, and Israel. The American literature, but for a few descriptive accounts, is limited almost exclusively to studies of white, usually middle class, persons. How other socioeconomic, racial, and ethnic groups react psychologically, socially, and biologically to bereavement is not known. Thus, it is unclear how generalizable and universal the current knowledge base is; this makes it difficult to develop intervention strategies that are appropriate to the needs of minority groups.

To refine this knowledge, research on the biology of grieving is also needed. Grief produces major perturbations in the respiratory, autonomic, and endocrine systems and may substantially alter cardiovascular and immune function as well. Much of the existing biologic research has been concerned simply with documenting these changes in animals and humans. It is time now to focus on clinically relevant physiologic changes in humans in order to understand better the mechanisms by which reactions to bereavement might result in actual illness.

In particular, more information is needed on the long-term effects of loss in order to understand how physiologic responses change over the course of grieving and how responses to loss compare with responses to other stressful situations. Additional studies are needed on the basic neurophysiologic parameters of grief responses in order to more fully understand the susceptibility of bereaved subjects to disease. The relationship between the responses to loss and responses to other life stresses, and detailed comparisons of the neuroendocrine and other biologic changes accompanying grief and depression, are needed. Multidisciplinary studies should be conducted of the relationships between the intertwined but not fully congruent behavioral, psychosocial, and biologic processes. This expanded knowledge of physiologic processes following bereavement and their relationship to other responses will contribute to the development of appropriate preventive interventions.

Most studies, whether biologic or psychologic, focus on the first year of bereavement. But because most people now die of chronic illness with forewarning for their families, the period of anticipatory grieving before the death deserves rigorous study. Furthermore, because it seems clear that for many people the grieving process continues beyond a year, studies should track bereaved individuals for a longer period of time. Thus, more prospective longitudinal studies that begin before and run for several years after bereavement are needed.

Traditionally, health consequences have been studied in individuals, but there is a growing realization that the individual's reactions may be based partly on interactions with the individual's most intimate group, which usually is the family. The death of one member will affect each and every other member as well as the family system as a whole. Thus, following bereavement, the changes in roles, relationships, and functioning within the family could lead to symptoms or disease in one or more members. In order to fully understand this process, prospective studies of entire families are needed.

Finally, all research on bereavement—epidemiologic, biologic, psychosocial, and intervention studies—has suffered from certain methodologic shortcomings. This research has been hampered by the lack of agreement concerning predictor variables and outcomes—what parameters are appropriate to measure, how to measure them, and what to consider as endpoints. So long as researchers make idiosyncratic decisions about these issues, comparisons across studies can be made only tentatively. Scientists from the many professional disciplines involved in bereavement research need to develop a consensus about which antecedent variables and outcomes to measure so that future studies will be more fully comparable.

Although a great deal is known about various aspects of bereavement and its consequences, most of it is discipline-specific. Isolated findings from psychology and psychiatry and from the biologic, medical, and social sciences each tell part of the story. But until more good multidisciplinary studies are done, the bereavement process and the mechanisms that explain it cannot be fully understood. Without such studies, the interactions between risk factors will remain unclear and it will not be possible to confidently identify groups at high risk. Good cross-disciplinary longitudinal studies also will provide the foundations for intervention strategies that are appropriate to the range of needs of bereaved individuals.

Research on Intervention Strategies

There is a paucity of good outcome data regarding the efficacy of any of the major types of bereavement interventions—mutual support, hospices, psychotherapy, and drug therapy. Conclusions about the applicability and effectiveness of specific interventions cannot be drawn from current data.

A broad research initiative is needed to study the impact of various psychosocial and pharmacologic interventions on the course and consequences of bereavement. Such research should be conducted in the awareness of cultural diversity and individual variations in reaction to bereavement. It should be specific to age, sex, social class, ethnicity, nature of the loss, and phase of bereavement. The impact of interventions on the acute distress of bereavement, on social as well as biologic functioning, and on health are some of the outcomes that deserve study. Research initiatives in this area should encourage cooperation among program administrators, clinicians, and researchers from several disciplines so that carefully controlled studies can be conducted.

In the case of drug therapies, the lack of research is striking. There have been virtually no controlled trials on the efficacy of commonly prescribed hypnotics and minor tranquilizers or on the use of antidepressants with the bereaved. Neither the immediate nor the long-term effects of using a drug therapy alone or in conjunction with a psychosocial intervention are known.

Although at the present time many specific gaps exist in our understanding of the bereavement process, it is time to begin to put the entire puzzle together—to link research on mechanisms, processes, and outcomes to the identification of groups at high risk for adverse outcomes, and to determine the best way to help individuals who have lost someone with whom they had close emotional ties.

REFERENCES

1. Osterweis M, Solomon F, Green M (Eds): Bereavement: Reactions, Consequences, and Care. A Report of the Institute of Medicine, National Academy of Sciences. Washington, DC, National Academy Press, 1984
2. Lindemann E: Symptomatology and management of acute grief. Am J Psychiatry 101:141-148, 1944
3. Raphael B: The Anatomy of Bereavement. New York, Basic Books, 1983
4. Silverman PR: Bereavement as a normal life transition, in Social Work with the Dying Patient and the Family. Edited by Prichard E, Collard J, Orcutt B, et al. New York, Columbia University Press, 1977
5. Elizur E, Kaffman M: Children's bereavement reactions following death of the father. J Am Acad Child Psychiatry 21:474-480, 1982
6. Bowlby J: Attachment and Loss, vol 3; Loss. New York, Basic Books, 1980
7. Kraus AS, Lilienfeld AM: Some epidemiologic aspects of the high mortality rate in the young widowed group. J Chronic Dis 10:207-217, 1959
8. Helsing KJ, Szklo M: Mortality after bereavement. Am J Epidemiol 114: 41-52, 1981
9. Cox PR, Ford JR: The mortality of widows shortly after widowhood. Lancet 1:163-164, 1964
10. Clayton PJ, Darvish JS: Course of depressive symptoms following the stress of bereavement, in Stress and Mental Disorder. Edited by Barrett JE. New York, Raven Press, 1979
11. Parkes CM, Weiss RS: Recovery from Bereavement. New York, Basic Books, 1983
12. Vachon MLS, Sheldon AR, Lancee WJ, et al: Correlates of enduring distress patterns following bereavement: social network, life situation, and personality. Psychol Med 12:783-788, 1982
13. Broadhead WE, Kaplan BH, James SA, et al: The epidemiologic evidence for a relationship between social support and health. Am J Epidemiol 117:521-537, 1983
14. Elliott GR, Eisdorfer C (Eds): Stress and Human Health: A Study by the Institute of Medicine, National Academy of Sciences. New York, Springer, 1982
15. Schmale A, Iker H: The psychological setting of uterine cervical cancer. Ann NY Acad Sci 125:794-801, 1965

16. Greene WA: Disease response to life stress. J Am Med Wom Assoc 20:133-140, 1965
17. Raphael B: Preventive intervention with the recently bereaved. Arch Gen Psychiatry 34:1450-1454, 1977
18. Forrest GC, Standish E, Baum JD: Support after perinatal death: a study of support and counselling after perinatal bereavement. Br Med J 285:1475-1479, 1982
19. Silverman PR: Widowhood and preventive intervention. Family Coordinator 21:95-102, 1972
20. Morgan D: Not all sadness can be treated with antidepressants. W Va Med J 76:136-137, 1980

[1] The Institute of Medicine was chartered in 1970 by the National Academy of Sciences to enlist distinguished members of appropriate professions in the examination of policy matters pertaining to the health of the public. In this, the Institute acts under both the Academy's 1863 congressional charter responsibility to be an adviser to the federal government, and its own initiative in identifying issues of medical care, research, and education.

[2] Committee members included Morris Green, M.D. (Chair), Indiana University; Eric Cassell, M.D., Cornell University; Paula Clayton, M.D., University of Minnesota; David S. Greer, M.D., Brown University; Jules Hirsch, M.D., The Rockefeller University; Myron A. Hofer, M.D., New York State Psychiatric Institute; Jimmie Holland, M.D., Memorial Sloan-Kettering Hospital, New York; Mardi Horowitz, M.D., University of California, San Francisco; Berton H. Kaplan, Ph.D., University of North Carolina at Chapel Hill; Marie Killilea, Johns Hopkins School of Hygiene and Public Health; Arthur Kleinman, M.D., Harvard Medical School; Gerald L. Klerman, M.D., Massachusetts General Hospital; Gerald Koocher, Ph.D., Children's Hospital Medical Center, Boston; Ida M. Martinson, R.N., Ph.D., University of California, San Francisco; Jack H. Medalie, M.D., M.P.H., Case Western Reserve University; Joan W. Mullaney, D.S.W., Catholic University of America; Robert F. Murray, Jr., M.D., Howard University; George H. Pollock, M.D., Institute for Psychoanalysis, Chicago; Theodore Shapiro, M.D., Cornell University; Robert S. Weiss, Ph.D., University of Massachusetts; William Wendt, S.T.D., St. Francis Center, Washington, D.C.

Chapter 2

Unresolved Grief

Sidney Zisook, M.D.

Chapter 2

Unresolved Grief

Bereavement is a ubiquitous human experience that most individuals face several times in their lives. Estimates of one-year incidence rates of bereavement in the general population range from five to nine percent (1–3). Although most bereaved individuals get over their grief and ultimately do well (uncomplicated grief), a significant minority develop morbid complications. Despite the large number of investigations on the course and outcome of grief through the years, the boundaries between normal or uncomplicated grief and pathological mourning often remain unclear. The distinction, however, may be clinically significant as "normal" grief is considered self-limited, relatively benign, and not amenable to psychotherapeutic intervention; whereas pathological grief may be associated with enormous social, psychological, and medical morbidity (4) and may warrant intensive intervention (5–12). This chapter summarizes relevant bereavement literature with a particular emphasis on the author's own research efforts to better demarcate "normal" from pathological bereavement.

Beginning with Freud's *Mourning and Melancholia*, several descriptions of normative grief and bereavement have appeared in the psychiatric literature over the past century. Freud identified four distinguishing features of "normal" mourning: a profoundly painful dejection, the loss of capacity to adopt new love objects, the inhibition of activity or turning away from activity not connected with thoughts of the loved person, and the loss of interest in the outside world insofar as it does not recall the deceased. Furthermore, Freud distinguished mourning from melancholia by the absence of ambivalent feelings about the deceased and significant disturbances in self-esteem in mourning (13). Reporting on observations of 101 survivors of the Coconut Grove fire in Boston, Eric Lindemann subsequently

---

This chapter is a revision of the article "Unresolved Grief." Reprinted by permission of the Editor of the *American Journal of Psychoanalysis* 45(4):370-379, 1985.

defined five characteristics "pathonomonic" of grief: somatic distress, preoccupation with images of the deceased, guilt, hostility, and loss of customary patterns of conduct. To these he added a sixth, shown by patients who border on pathological reactions, namely the appearance of traits of the deceased in behavior of the bereaved (identification phenomena) (14).

Building on Freud's and Lindemann's work, Engel proposed that grief was a disease state with a predictable course and specific symptoms (15). Focusing primarily on psychopathological symptoms, Clayton subsequently found crying, sleep disturbances, and depressed mood as cardinal symptoms of the bereavement period, and that 45 percent of widows suffer from a major depressive disorder within the first 13 months of the death of a spouse. In her study, the depression of widowhood was distinguished by the absence of disturbed self-esteem, guilt, motor retardation, fear of losing one's mind, suicide attempts, past personal or family history of depression, or seeking professional help for the depression (16). On the other hand, Maddison and Viola found a significant proportion of bereaved women did seek professional consultation for the "depression" of widowhood and found the following symptoms more common in the bereaved than in married women: nervousness, depression, fear of nervous breakdown, feelings of panic, persistent fears, "peculiar" thoughts, nightmares, insomnia, trembling, appetite changes, loss of weight, reduced work capacity, fatigue, and a number of other somatic symptoms not heretofore associated with grief (17).

Our own staging of the grief process, similar to those proposed above, includes at least three partially overlapping but distinct stages: 1) an initial period of *shock*, disbelief and denial; 2) an intermediate *acute mourning* period of acute somatic and emotional discomfort and social withdrawal; and 3) a culminating period of *resolution* (18) (see Table 1).

The first stage, *shock*, lasts from hours to weeks and is characterized by varying degrees of disbelief and denial of loss. Feeling numb and paralyzed, the bereaved cannot believe the death is real. Mourning rites and the gathering of family and friends facilitate passage through this stage.

A second stage, *acute mourning*, begins when the death is acknowledged cognitively and emotionally. In the *intense feeling* phase of this stage, painful awareness of the loss occurs in periodic waves of intense emotional and often somatic discomfort. These waves bring on uncontrollable sighing and sobbing and are often attended by a feeling of tightness in the throat, a shortness of breath, an empty feeling in the abdomen, fatigue, restlessness, purposeless activity, and a subjective sense of stress experienced as exhaustion, weakness, and sadness. Because these periods may be precipitated by visitors who drop by and talk about the deceased, the bereaved soon enter a second phase of acute mourning, *social withdrawal*. They may avoid visitations in an attempt to suppress painful awareness of the loss. They tend to feel irritable or angry, avoid friends, miss work, and experience an emotional distancing from people. In searching the time before the death for evidence of failure in the relationship to the deceased, the bereaved often become abnormally consumed with anger, guilt, or both, and thus enter the third phase of acute mourning, *identification with the deceased*. Their entire thought content and affect become bound up with the dead relative, spouse, or friend. Often the mourners transiently adopt the mannerisms, habits, and even somatic symptoms of the deceased (14).

Acute mourning may last several months before being gradually replaced by a slow resolution of the grieving with return of the feeling of well-being and the ability to get on with living (4, 14). In this *resolution stage*, the bereaved recognize what the loss has meant to them, that they have grieved, and begin to shift attention to the world around them. Memories are, and loneliness may be, a part of that world, but the deceased with their ills and problems are not. The hallmark of the resolution stage is the ability of the bereaved to recognize that they have grieved and now can return to work, re-experience pleasure, and seek the companionship and love of others.

Often, however, the grieving process does not follow the course detailed above. Occasionally, that process becomes deviant, and one or more of the phases of grief is absent, delayed, intensified, or prolonged (18). The clinical syndromes that characterize departure from normal grieving have been described by various observers as

Table 1. Stages of Grief

I. Shock—denial and disbelief
II. Acute mourning
    A. Intense feeling states: crying spells, guilt, shame, depression, anorexia, insomnia, irritability, emptiness, and fatigue
    B. Social withdrawal: preoccupation with health, inability to sustain usual work, family, and personal relationships
    C. Identification with the deceased: transient adoption of habits, mannerisms, and somatic symptoms of the deceased
III. Resolution—acceptance of loss, awareness of having grieved, return to well-being, and ability to recall the deceased without subjective pain

morbid (14), atypical (12), pathological (19), complicated (20), absent (21), abnormal (22), neurotic (23), depression of widowhood (16), grief related facsimile illness (24), or unresolved (25, 26). We have previously conceptualized such syndromes as nonresolution of the grief process, or unresolved grief, whereby phases of the grief process, when incompletely resolved, are associated with relatively specific clinical syndromes such as depression or "grief related facsimile illness" (18, 24, 25). The frequency of unresolved grief is unknown and depends on diverse factors such as the population studied and definitions of the term, but reported estimates range from 10 to 25 percent (18, 26, 27).

Since unresolved grief is such a frequent disorder with significant medical, psychological, and social morbidity, and since its recognition depends on a clear understanding of the phenomenology and course of "normal," expected, or uncomplicated bereavement, we have been involved in developing an instrument to better describe, measure, and operationalize the grief process. We first developed the Texas Inventory of Grief, a 14-item self-report scale (28). Based on the literature of normative and atypical grief reactions as well as the clinical experience of the authors, the original 14-item inventory was expanded to 58 items. To obtain normative data the instrument was sent to friends and colleagues around the country so that they could ask one or two friends or neighbors who had lost a relative or close friend to complete the questionnaire. The respondents were asked to give their age, sex, race, religion, educational level, relationship to the deceased, length of time since the death, and age of the deceased. They were asked to check one of five responses on each of 24 items related to their feelings when the person died and 34 items pertaining to present feelings. Three items that most closely approximated those characteriestics used clinically by us to help identify unresolved grief were chosen to comprise an unresolved grief index: 1) I feel I have grieved for the person who died; 2) Now I can talk about the person without discomfort; and 3) I feel I have adjusted well to the loss. In addition to the Grief Inventory and the Unresolved Grief Index, each respondent was asked to complete a Zung Self-Rating Depression Scale. Much of the rest of this paper is based upon the results of that survey (27, 29, 30).

COURSE OF UNCOMPLICATED GRIEF

One of the most common definitions of pathological grief is mourning that is either delayed or prolonged, yet there is little agreement regarding the time course of "normal" bereavement. In general, the expected time course for what would be accepted as "normal" is broadening through the years. Lindemann, studying the symptomatology and management of acute grief, felt that the uncomplicated and undisturbed grief reaction could be settled in a period of four to six weeks (14). Several years later Engel measured uncomplicated grief in terms of months (15). Bornstein found 35 percent of bereaved widows were depressed within one month and 17 percent still clinically depressed after 13 months following the death of a loved one, with symptoms of crying spells, weight loss, and insomnia continuing to be common (31). Studying a group of London widows 13 months after bereavement, Parkes found only three women who could look at the past with pleasure and to the future with optimism; contrarily, most described themselves as sad, poorly adjusted, depressed, often thinking about their deceased husbands, having clear visual memories of them, and still grieving a great deal of the time. Thus, Parkes concluded that the process of grieving was still going on after 13 months and that the question of how long grief lasts was still unanswered (32). Finally, Goin suggested that not only do many people maintain a "timeless" emotional involvement with the deceased, but also that this attachment often represents healthy adaptation to the loss of a valued loved one (33).

In our own study, grief did not simply end at six weeks, six months, or even six years. Although several features seemed to peak within one to two years, particularly those dealing with the dysphoria, many symptoms and behaviors continued to be present for years, perhaps indefinitely. All items in our grief inventory were endorsed by at least some people even 10 or more years after bereavement. The most commonly endorsed items after 10 years were: no one will ever take his/her place in my life; I very much miss the person; I have never known a better person; sometimes I dream about him/her; I can't avoid thinking about him/her; I feel it is unfair that he/she died; even now it is painful to recall memories of him/her; things and people around me still remind me of him/her; I still get upset when I think about him/her; at times I still feel that I need to cry for him/her; and, at times I feel as though he/she is still with me (29). Thus it seems that some aspects of grief work may never end for a significant proportion of otherwise normal bereaved individuals.

SYNDROMES ASSOCIATED WITH UNRESOLVED GRIEF

In previous reports we have postulated several pathological syndromes associated with nonresolution of any of the stages of grief (18, 25). Thus, for example, nonresolution of the first stage, shock, may lead to psychotic denial of the loss on the one hand, or chronic hope for the return of the deceased on the other (Table 2). If the progress of bereavement is arrested in the final stage, resolution, the bereaved become chronic mourners; their attention becomes fixed on the deceased and the events surrounding the death, rather than being turned back to the world at large. Chronic mourning may be more likely to occur when the relationship between the bereaved and the deceased was very close, or where social support is lacking and friends and relatives are not available to share sorrow over the extended period of time needed for grieving (34). Nonresolution of any of the three phases of the second stage of bereavement, acute mourning, also leads to specific syndromes such as depression, chronic illness behavior or hypochondriasis, and grief related facsimile illness. These syndromes will be discussed in more detail in the following subsections.

Depression

The relationship between loss and depression is well established. As recently reviewed by Lloyd (35), childhood bereavement, and a variety of adult losses, including bereavement, increase the risk for depression. In a series of studies by Clayton and associates (16, 31, 36–40), a number of depressive symptoms were found to be common accompaniments of widowhood. This depression could not be distinguished from the depression of the nonbereaved controls on the basis of symptoms alone. However, the depression following death of a spouse was not more common in women than in men, not associated with a family history of depression or previous depressive episodes, not likely to be treated by a psychiatrist, and not associated with a subjective sense of being ill. There is also a suggestion in the literature that depression may not be due not only to the loss itself,

Table 2. Syndromes Associated with Nonresolution of the Stages of Grief

Stage (phase)	Resolution	Nonresolution
I. Shock—Denial	Acceptance	Psychotic denial
II. Acute Mourning		
A. Intense Feeling States	Equanimity	Depression
B. Withdrawal	Reinvolvement	Hypochondriasis
C. Identification	Individuation	Grief related facsimile illness
III. Resolution	Work, love, play	Chronic Mourning

but also to the relationship between the deceased and the bereaved and to the way the bereaved dealt with the loss. For example, Deutsch stated that when mourning does not follow its normal course and is unexpressed, which is particularly likely to occur when the relationship with the deceased is filled with ambivalence and guilt, it will find its expression in some other way, as in depression (21). Lindemann also found depression could be the result of delayed or distorted reaction to bereavement (14). Similarly, Anderson found depression to be a more likely consequence of bereavement when the relationship with the lost object was precarious and profoundly ambivalent (41).

Our study, too, suggested a relationship between unresolved grief and depression. Individuals with evidence of unresolved grief were significantly more depressed as measured by total Zung scores and numerous items on the Zung scale. Although no cause and effect relationship could be defined, it did appear that persons who reported that they had grieved, adjusted to the loss, and could talk about the deceased without difficulty were less likely to be depressed than those who indicated that they had not fully grieved (27). Thus, while depressive symptoms are a common and relatively self-limited aspect of "normal" bereavement, a full blown depressive illness may be more related to nonresolution of grief than simply to the loss itself.

Chronic Illness Behavior and Hypochondriasis

Failure to resolve the second phase of acute mourning, the social withdrawal phase, can lead to chronic illness behavior and hypochondriasis. Patients whose grieving does not pass this phase appear preoccupied with health and unable to reinvest interest or energy in social relationships. More then 20 percent of our sample remember feeling empty, finding it hard to work well, unable to keep up with normal activities, and concerned about their own health after the death of their loved one (30). Even years after the death, many of our respondents still felt preoccupied with thoughts of the deceased, felt physically ill when thinking about him or her, and felt that their health had declined since the death (29). In a variant of this syndrome, medical complaints appear or escalate either on the anniversary of the death or when the bereaved reach the age at which the deceased became ill (42, 43). Over a quarter of our population still felt upset on the anniversary of their loss (29). Both chronic pain patients (44) and polysurgical patients (45) have been found to have a high incidence of unresolved grief reactions and often present to the physician with somatic complaints on such anniversaries.

Grief Related Facsimile Illness

If the bereaved do not successfully work through the identification phase of acute mourning, they may complain not merely of various physical symptoms like the group just discussed, but may report the specific symptoms suffered by the deceased. Identification with a family member or loved one who has died is a normal part of grieving and is usually transient. Freud considered identification with the lost object to be a critical aspect of all mourning (13). Abraham stressed the intrapsychic meaning of identification (46), and Loewald noted its adaptive value (47). When the identification phase is not resolved, however, the bereaved may develop "grief related facsimile illness" (24); that is, they experience enduring signs and symptoms of the terminal illness of the deceased. These patients seem literally to keep the lost person with them—to suffer their illness or problems rather than acknowledge the more painful loss. Lindemann had described identification phenomena as a characteristic of normal bereavement but also one that borders on pathologic. "There is the appearance of the deceased in the behavior of the bereaved, especially symptoms shown during the last illness . . . a preoccupation with symptoms . . . now displayed to their own bodies . . . by identification . . . this type of patient appears in medical clinics and is often labeled hypochodriacal or hysteric" (14, p. 142). Parkes, too, considered excessively prolonged or intense identification phenomena pathological (12). We have previously reported on a series of 10 patients, all of whom presented with a constellation of symptoms or behaviors almost identical with that ascribed to the deceased's last illness, and coined this syndrome grief related facsimile illness (24). All 10 patients demonstrated features consistent with an arrest of the uncomplicated grief response, all were treated ineffectively and inappropriately by medical, surgical, or psychiatric means prior to the recognition of the syndrome, all were referred for reasons other than complications of grief, and all either recovered or were significantly improved during treatment aimed at facilitating the grief response. In our recently completed survey, 16 percent of the respondents remembered beginning to do things the way the deceased had done them shortly after the death and 20 percent were afraid that they may have had the same illness or accident as the deceased (30); more than 10 percent felt that they had become more like the person who had died, felt just like him/her, and felt they had the same illness; while almost as many bereaved persons admitted to acquiring the habits and interests of the deceased or having pain in the same area of their body as him/her. None of those items changed significantly over time. Thus, such identification symptoms, when present, tend to remain (29).

SUMMARY

This chapter reviews the literature on bereavement and, with particular emphasis on the authors' own work, describes three syndromes which seem related to nonresolution of distinct phases of the grief process. The possibility of unresolved grief should receive a high index of suspicion for the patient with otherwise unexplainable depression, chronic illness behavior, or symptoms similar to a deceased relative or friend. When any of these syndromes are identified, it is useful to ask the patient whom (s)he has lost, how (s)he has lost them, how (s)he felt about the loss, whether (s)he felt (s)he grieved, whether (s)he still cries or feels the need to cry, and whether (s)he has adjusted. The answer to these questions—both verbal and nonverbal—will help identify unresolved grief when present and may help guide specific interventions.

On the other hand, our studies have suggested that unresolved grief is a somewhat overly simplistic concept. Most, if not all, people never totally resolve their grief; significant aspects of the bereavement process go on for years after the loss, even in otherwise normal patients. For some, identification syndromes continue. Others may continue to feel the presence of the deceased or have daily visions of him/her. Still others may feel the pain, anger, and guilt for years after the death. At what point and to what degree these behaviors and symptoms become medical or psychiatric concerns, become pathological, or predispose to serious medical, psychological, or social complications is still unclear. Investigations into these unreported areas have been initiated, and, we trust, will lead to clinically useful answers.

References

1. Imboden JB, Canter A, Cluff L: Separation experience and health records in a group of normal adults. Psychom Med 25:433-440, 1963
2. Frost NR, Clayton PJ: Bereavement and psychiatric hospitalization. Arch Gen Psychiatry 34:1172-1175, 1977
3. Pearlin L, Lieberman M: Social sources of distress, in Research in Community Health. Edited by Simms R. Greenwich, Conn, JAI Press, 1979
4. Klerman GL, Izen JE: The effects of bereavement and grief on physical health and well-being. Adv Psychosom Med 9:66-104, 1977
5. Shuchter SR: How the family physician can help patients cope with grief. Medical Aspects of Human Sexuality 18:30-54, 1984
6. Mawson D, Marks IM, Ramm L, et al: Guided mourning for morbid grief: a controlled study. Br J Psychiatry 138:185-193, 1981
7. Vachon MLS, Lyall WAL, Rogers J, et al: A controlled study of self-help intervention for widows. Am J Psychiatry 137:1380-1384, 1980
8. Parkes CM: Bereavement counselling: does it work? Br Med J 7:3-6, 1980
9. Raphael B: Preventive intervention with the recently bereaved. Arch Gen Psychiatry 34:1450-1545, 1977
10. Raphael B: The management of pathological grief. Australian NZ J Psychiatry 9:173-180, 1975
11. Volkan VD: A study of patient's "re-grief work" through dreams, psychological tests and psychoanalysis. Psychoanal Q 45:255-273, 1971
12. Parkes CM: Bereavement: Studies of Grief in Adult Life. New York, International Universities Press, 1972
13. Freud S: Mourning and melancholia (1917), in The Complete Psychological Works, Standard Edition, vol. 14. Translated and edited by Strachey J. London, Hogarth Press, 1961
14. Lindemann E: Symptomatology and management of acute grief. Am J Psychiatry 101:141-148, 1944
15. Engel GL: Is grief a disease? Psychosom Med 23:18-22, 1961
16. Clayton PJ, Halikas JA, Maurice WL: The depression of widowhood. Br J Psychiatry 120:71-76, 1972
17. Maddison DC, Viola A: The health of widows in the year following bereavement. J Psychosom Res 12:297, 1968
18. DeVaul RA, Zisook S, Faschingbauer TR: Clinical aspects of grief and bereavement. Primary Care 6:391-402, 1979

19. Volkan V: The recognition and prevention of pathological grief. Virginia Medical Monthly 99:535-540, 1972

20. White RB, Gathman LT: The syndrome of ordinary grief. Am Fam Physician 8:97-105, 1973

21. Deutsch H: Absence of grief. Psychoanal Q 6:12, 1937

22. Hackett TP: Recognizing and treating abnormal grief. Hospital Physician 1:49-54, 1974

23. Wahl CW: The differential diagnosis of normal and neurotic grief following bereavement. Psychosomatics 11:104-106, 1970

24. Zisook S, DeVaul RA: Grief related facsimile illness. Int J Psychiatry Med 7:329-336, 1977

25. DeVaul RA, Zisook S: Unresolved grief: clinical considerations. Postgrad Med 59:267, 1976

26. Lazare A: Unresolved grief in outpatient psychiatry, diagnosis and treatment. Edited by Lazare A. Baltimore, Williams and Wilkins, 1979

27. Zisook S, DeVaul RA: Grief, unresolved grief, and depression. Psychosomatics 24:247-256, 1983

28. Faschingbauer TR, DeVaul RA, Zisook S: Development of the Texas Inventory of Grief. Am J Psychiatry 134:696-698, 1977

29. Zisook S, DeVaul RA, Click MA: Measuring symtoms of grief and bereavement. Am J Psychiatry 139: 1593-1594, 1982

30. Zisook S, DeVaul RA: Measuring acute grief. Psychiatric Medicine 2:169-176, 1984

31. Bornstein PE, Clayton PJ, Halikas JA, et al: The depression of widowhood after thirteen months. Br J Psychiatry 122:561-567, 1973

32. Parkes CM: The first year of bereavement: a longitudinal study of the reaction of London widows to the death of their husbands. Psychiatry 33:444-466, 1971

33. Goin MK, Burgoyne RW, Goin JM: Timeless attachment to a dead relative. Am J Psychiatry 136:988-989, 1979

34. Schwab JJ, Chalmers JM, Conroy SJ, et al: Studies in grief: a preliminary report in Bereavement: Its Psychosocial Aspects. Edited by Schoenberg B, Gerber I. New York, Columbia University Press, 1975

35. Lloyd C: Life events and depressive disorder reviewed, Parts I and II. Arch Gen Psychiatry 37:529-535, 1980

36. Clayton P, Desmarais L, Winokur G: A study of normal bereavement. Am J Psychiatry 125:168-178, 1968

37. Clayton PJ, Halikas JA, Maurice WL: The bereavement of the widowed. Diseases of the Nervous System 32:597-604, 1971

38. Clayton PJ, Halikas JA, Maurice WL: Anticipatory grief and widowhood. Br J Psychiatry 122:47-51, 1973

39. Clayton PJ, Herjanic M, Murphy GE, et al: Mourning and depression: their similarities and differences. Can J Psychiatry 19:309-312, 1974

40. Clayton PJ: Mortality and morbidity in the first year of widowhood. Arch Gen Psychiatry 30:747-750, 1974

41. Anderson C: Aspects of pathological grief and mourning. Int J Psychoanal 30:48-55, 1948

42. Hilgard JR, Newman MF: Anniversaries in mental illness. Psychiatry 22:113-122, 1959

43. Musaph H: Anniversary disease. Psychother Psychosom 22:325-330, 1973

44. DeVaul RA, Zisook S, Stuart HJ: Patients with psychogenic pain. J Fam Pract 4:53-55, 1977

45. DeVaul RA, Faillace LA: Persistent pain and illness insistence: a medical profile of proneness to surgery. Am J Surg 135:828-833, 1978

46. Abraham K: A short study of the development of the libido: selected papers. London, Institute of Psychoanalysis and Hogarth Press, 1927

47. Loewald HW: Internalization, separation, mourning and the superego. Psychoanal Q 31:483-504, 1962

Chapter 3

A Multidimensional Model of Spousal Bereavement

Stephen R. Shuchter, M.D.
Sidney Zisook, M.D.

Chapter 3

A Multidimensional Model of Spousal Bereavement

The death of a spouse can precipitate some of the deepest anguish and most profound disruptions that human beings are likely to experience. Such a loss usually has an impact upon every aspect of the survivor's life, with significant effects seen in his or her immediate mental and emotional responses; in efforts to cope with anguish; in his or her remaining relationships; in health and functioning; and in his or her sense of identity. This chapter presents a multidimensional model of the effects of spousal bereavement as a guide to understanding the many levels of the grief experience, and as a model for the assessment and treatment of clinical problems that arise at such times.

MENTAL AND EMOTIONAL DISRUPTIONS

The acute reactions to loss have been described by numerous observers (1–4) and include the initial period of shock followed by the intense emotional pangs of grief that accompany the realization of the death. The "shock" may be experienced as a sense of numbness or unreality and it may have a dream-like quality. Under the influence of this state of detachment, the individual is protected from the impact of a new reality, and may remain in this state for periods lasting from minutes to days. Some widowed persons have described functioning for weeks and months in this state, but that is exceptional.

Shock gives way to the waves and pangs of intense grief. People become flooded with such emotions, often manifest through autonomic discharge and the experiences of "heartache" and a "knife in the gut." These waves occur intermittently, frequently initiated by some concrete reminder of the death. They can occur suddenly and unexpectedly, precipitated by an endless number of sources: contact

---

This chapter has been adapted from Shuchter SR: Dimensions of Grief: Adjustment to the Death of a Spouse. San Francisco, Jossey-Bass 1986

with mutual friends, a memory or an image, a song or picture or article of clothing. Each "trigger" is met with the same pain. Over time the intensity and frequency of such experiences of grief will usually diminish, but they are likely to appear, at least occasionally, for months and even years. At "special times"—holidays, birthdays, anniversaries—they may be ushered in with greater intensity.

As the reality of the death sinks in, the survivor often experiences an increasing sense of loss. The sense of loss is not simply for the person who has died, but also for that part of the survivor which was "connected" to the spouse and to the hopes, dreams, and plans for a future with the person who has died. The missing, longing, yearning, and searching become part of the survivor's life. The usual course of such experiences is that after a period of greater intensity, there is a gradual lessening over time.

Many, though not all, of the newly bereaved go through a period of time in which anger becomes a significant part of their grief. While the essence of such anger probably lies in the loss and pain, the focus of the anger and the forms that it can take are variable. The anger may be felt toward the dead spouse for unhealthy ways of living, or as a legacy of anger having to do with the relationship. Usually, however, it is felt as a response to being abandoned and left in the lurch. The survivors may find themselves angry at their spouses' doctors for acts of commission or omission; at God or fate; or at their family or friends. The anger may also take the form of a sense of exploitation by society and envy of those who have a relationship which they don't.

Another frequent and painful affect of the bereaved is guilt, whether it is in the form of survival guilt or a sense of responsibility for the death or suffering of their spouse. Usually, this sense of guilt, especially the more irrational feelings, are transient. Later, as the survivor makes new emotional attachments, there may appear a new form of guilt: a sense of betrayal. Again, this is usually transient.

Anxiety and fearfulness about both the imagined and real threats to the newly bereaved person's existence become a regular part of life. Those who have been more autonomous and independent may feel better prepared to face the world alone, but even the most adaptive people experience some anxiety while facing the uncertainty of the future as well as the realistic hardships created by long-standing illness, large medical bills, loss of income, lack of insurance, and concerns about the welfare of surviving children.

Among the disruptive legacies of the death of a spouse are the intrusive images which force their way into the minds of the survivor. These often occur in the form of "instant replays" of the circumstances of the death or images of the dying spouse in scenes of deterioration or suffering. Particularly in the early weeks and months of bereavement these intrusive images can create overwhelming distress.

Mental disorganization is another feature of bereavement that is highly distressing and that may interfere significantly with the survivor's capacity to function. People experience varying degrees of distractibility and poor concentration, confusion, forgetfulness, and lack of clarity and coherence. Contributing to this disorganization may be rapidly changing emotional states produced by acute stress. Certainly such phenomena can be part of a depression, and if they persist beyond the first few months are likely to be manifestations of "true" depression.

Apathy, independent of other depressive symptoms, may also appear, often after some delay. This may seem quite foreign and dystonic to a usually active person.

It must be remembered that many people die after prolonged illness, particularly cancer, where there has been significant deterioration, pain, and suffering for both the dying and surviving spouses. Under such circumstances, the survivors are likely to experience a sense of relief: from their own suffering, from the suffering of their spouse, and at times from other hardships or conflicts that were an integral part of their relationship. Often a sense of guilt may accompany this relief.

Throughout the early weeks and months of bereavement, survivors frequently find themselves in fluctuating states of turmoil associated with the unpredictable emergence of any of these emotional and cognitive changes. They may feel overwhelmed, out of control, like they are "going crazy." Healthy, generally adaptive people may never have experienced such an emotional roller coaster and find it very disconcerting to be unable to assert control over their internal lives. Some people find this aspect of their bereavement as upsetting as the other changes.

COPING WITH EMOTIONAL PAIN

Faced with the onslaught of recurrent, often unpredictable, and usually disruptive emotional and cognitive states, people find ways to protect themselves from such distress. Survivors will utilize their customary defenses where possible, but usually resort to developmentally more primitive ones and to the use of multiple defenses.

We have just described numbness as an emotional state, but its essence is the extreme detachment or dissociation between the the intellect and emotions. Accompanying this state, particularly in the early phases, is a sense of disbelief which lasts for months despite the obvious perceptual and intellectual awareness of the death.

Survivors can exert conscious emotional control through suppression in many situations in which they deem loss of control socially inappropriate, or in situations in which they fear that they will succumb to their feelings. Others, on an unconscious basis—though usually for the same reasons—utilize isolation of affect as an extension of their customary way of dealing with uncomfortable feelings. The effectiveness of these defenses is highly variable, depending on the circumstances and the intensity of the stimulus. Furthermore, emotional constriction, while it has as its primary adaptive value the protection of the person from his or her affect, can interfere with the expression and catharsis which are seen intuitively as necessary to the emotional and physical well-being of the surviving spouse.

Widows and widowers utilize a variety of "altered perspectives" to help mitigate against their loss and suffering. Intellectualization and rationalization serve as major means of protection, particularly the latter. There are several recurrent themes which become prevalent in the thinking of the bereaved, including: "He is better this way than to be suffering"; "Things could have been worse"; "We were lucky to have what we had."

One of the mainstays of the bereaved is the operation of their faith. This is a powerful and effective means of coping with death and seems to operate in a number of ways: it can facilitate acceptance, provide meaning, offer help and support through God, combat loneliness, and offer the bereaved a chance to reunite with their spouse in heaven.

Avoidance becomes standard in the repertoire of the bereaved. This is a quickly learned response that develops as soon as the survivor perceives, consciously or unconsciously, that a given stimulus serves as a "trigger" that sets off the painful feelings of grief. People may become unable to tolerate looking at pictures of their spouse; sleeping in their bed; keeping their spouse's belongings at home; driving by the hospital where their spouse died; talking with mutual friends; or going to the cemetery. In the extreme, avoidance can be as complete as the accidental exposures to reminders. More commonly, the survivors' capacities to tolerate such exposure will increase over time. They will find that they can "dose" themselves; that is, they can make efforts to expose themselves to such triggers for brief periods when they feel stronger.

Being busy—with work, school, housework, hobbies, or volunteer work—is another means of coping. Being busy allows the bereaved to invest themselves, focus their thoughts, and distract themselves from their grief. Their distraction often sharply contrasts with the return of grief at the end of the day when they arrive home to an empty house.

Radio, television, or reading become frequently used in day-to-day efforts of the bereaved to distract themselves. An advantage of radio and television is that they may provide a modicum of companionship through sound and pictures, which can combat loneliness. At times, however, material from the media may also serve as triggers.

Involvement with other people can be a very productive and adaptive way of dealing with one's grief. Relationships can provide support, comfort, and stave off loneliness. By investing in others, one focuses on others' needs rather than on one's own misery. Pets are an often forgotten resource whose value is apparent to many bereaved individuals. They can be objects of affection and caregiving as well as sources of love, appreciation, and companionship.

Indulgence in many nonproductive and even self-destructive means of coping with internal feeling states is frequent in the newly bereaved. The use of food, alcohol, tobacco, or even sex may take on compulsive features. The newly bereaved are particularly vulnerable to such maladaptive behaviors for many reasons. Their pain is powerful, their resistance is low, their sense of entitlement is high, and they often say to themselves, "Who cares?" Manic defenses, on the verge of clinical mania, may be expressed in other impulsive acts involving spending money or making drastic changes in their lives with regard to their homes, careers, or relationships in frantic efforts to ward off their pain.

THE CONTINUING RELATIONSHIP WITH THE DEAD SPOUSE

One of the most powerful means of coping with the death of a spouse is that which mitigates completely against the loss; that is, the ability of the survivor to keep the dead alive. Obviously, this does not occur in a literal sense, but through a variety of psychological mechanisms that permit survivors to maintain their ties to their dead spouses.

The identification of a specific location provides a sense of comfort and a place where the bereaved can visualize their spouse as continuing to have an existence. Most commonly this is in heaven, which further implies peace and the possibility of being reunited with their spouse.

Continuing contact with the spouse is experienced by the bereaved in a variety of forms: sensory evidence of a presence, including auditory, visual, and haptic hallucinations; an internal sense of the presence of their spouse to watch over, comfort, or protect them;

or communication between the living and the dead as a means of sharing, prayer, decision-making, and protection.

Symbolic representations provide a means of keeping the deceased alive by imbuing certain belongings, creations, or shared experiences with the spirit of memories of the deceased. These are frequently personal possessions that capture important attributes (a favorite robe, a garden tended by the deceased, tools or equipment associated with a vocational interest, a car) or symbols of their relationship together (a ring, their bed, or home). It must be remembered that most of these symbols of continuing contact are experienced ambivalently: they keep the person alive but also serve as reminders that he or she is gone and can thereby become painful triggers.

The living legacies that allow for continuity of these relationships can be seen through the often remarkable transformation that takes place as a result of the process of identification. The survivor may take on personality characteristics, habits, aesthetics, or even somatic symptoms of the deceased. While identification is an unconscious process, there are active, conscious means of perpetuating the deceased's existence. The dead spouse's wishes, expectations, or commitments may be carried out by the surviving spouse, often through endowments. There is no dearth of books on bereavement which are dedicated to a spouse whose death made the work possible. The most ubiquitous living legacies are those children whose genetic makeup recreate aspects of the person's appearance, mannerisms, or personality.

Our social and cultural rituals reinforce the individual's predisposition to perpetuate such connections. Tributes to the deceased are incorporated into most funeral services. Visitations to the gravesite prove to the bereaved, from the start of mourning, that the power of memory can serve as a means of staying connected: friends and family know this intuitively as they share their memories of the deceased with the bereaved and realize that the deceased remains alive through their emotions. The cemetery is often most evocative of both the painful awareness of the death and of the emotional connection that continues.

As time goes on the memories of most widowed people remain the most tangible and available sources of this continuing relationship. They may create a certain degree of distortion and embellishment of the realities surrounding the deceased. There is often a bittersweet quality associated with both the pain of a trigger and the comfort of its presence. During the early weeks and months of bereavement, the survivor may experience some difficulties in conjuring up images and memories of the deceased. This can be quite frightening. The fear that one cannot recapture a loved one may be further complicated under circumstances of a prolonged illness where the only memories and images available are the scenes of illness, helplessness, emaciation, or death. When positive memories appear down the road, they are met with tremendous relief. Similar desperation can occur when people find their memories fading away, intensifying their sense of loss or precipitating guilt for not caring enough.

Dreams of the bereaved may reveal the status of their relationships with the deceased. Most commonly, dreams of the spouse are retrieval in nature, reflecting the obvious wish that the spouse has returned: scenes of mundane life where the spouse simply exists. Other dreams reflect efforts to separate or the struggle to deal with the conflicts that were a part of their lives together.

The common thread that runs through all of these psychological phenomena is the effort to bring the deceased back to life in whatever form this can be accomplished.

DYSFUNCTION

Many studies have documented the heightened risk to health of spousal bereavement (5), particularly during the first year. While studies of mortality have yielded variable conclusions, the survivor's risk for depression, alcoholism, drug abuse, cardiovascular disease, and disorders of suppressed immune function (infection, cancer) all appear to increase after the death of a spouse. Somatic symptoms of distress are a fairly universal part of the acute reaction to grief and may be the source of the increased frequency with which the bereaved utilize health care.

Work performance may be significantly impaired as a natural consequence of a specific medical or psychiatric disorder. Even in the absence of such a disorder, acute grief frequently creates degrees of mental disorganization, confusion, anxiety, memory disturbances, and distractibility, which can significantly interfere with the person's capacity to perform a task. Contributing to this dysfunction are intrusive thoughts and images and strong emotional reactions to them. Later on, if a clinical depression evolves, it may reproduce many of these same disorganizing phenomena. Furthermore, when apathy appears, the loss of motivation about one's tasks will contribute to deteriorating function.

While social activity may be adaptive as the bereaved seek out others for support, involvement, and distraction, there are periods of time, particularly in early phases, where the grieving person may exhibit varying degrees of social inhibition, withdrawal, and isolation. This may be a primitive mechanism to protect and preserve precious emotional reserves in an individual whose survival is threatened. Its effects, however, may be to cut off resources of emotional support that may be essential to the bereaved.

Other forms of dysfunction involve both role changes and problems which are new, complicated, and seem overwhelming. These may include difficulties in driving a car alone, writing a check, caring for children or cooking meals, filing insurance claims, obtaining social security benefits, and so on.

CHANGES IN RELATIONSHIPS

One of the inevitable consequences of spousal bereavement is that the surviving spouse experiences significant changes in his or her relationships with other people. There may be greater closeness, a different meaning, an altered role or dynamic. Some relationships end while others begin, but all are affected by the death.

The most complex changes in relationships occur within the family. Where there are young children in the home, the surviving parent will have the task of helping these children cope with their grief. The structure of the family changes with shifting roles. Single parenting changes the sources of gratification and discipline. Where there are grown children, there may be conflicts in the expectations of the children and surviving parent, for good or ill. The surviving spouse may also be seen as the major support for older parents or in-laws and may have the responsibility of helping them grieve. With any family member, regardless of the nature of their prior relationships to the surviving spouse, there is an opportunity for growth and greater intimacy or, conversely, the possibility of conflict and disruption.

Friends may be major sources of support for the bereaved. They can reach out and give, or understand and accept the survivor's withdrawal, without being put off. Friends can offer practical help and emotional support by sharing the pain and allowing its free expression. There can also be great disappointment and potential disruption of relationships when friends are incapable of empathizing with the bereaved. This may occur from a strong need to deny that such a threat to their own marriages could exist, from an inability to tolerate the person's grief because of its intensity, or, at times, from projected sexual jealousy.

The bereaved may find themselves avoided, treated differently, feeling personally responsible, and rejected. Family as well as friends may allot an insufficient period of "permission" for the bereaved to express grief.

Out of the turmoil of bereavement, new friendships are often created with people who have experienced their own grief and are found to be more understanding and accepting of the widowed person's distress. For some, new romances occur with both the obvious advantages of intimacy and sexuality, and the conflicts which may be experienced in regard to feelings of betrayal, comparisons, the difficult process of dating, as well as the inevitable conflicts which are inherent in all relationships. Where remarriage occurs, there may be complications created by "blended" families. Even when a successful remarriage occurs, the experiences of grief do not end.

Sexual relationships, though often difficult for the newly bereaved to consider without conflict, are frequently developed both within and outside the context of marriage. This is not uncommon within a few months and is frequent by two years. Early in bereavement, especially when the death followed a prolonged illness where sexuality played a diminishing role, the survivor may have suppressed his or her sexual feelings long enough so that their reemergence is met with surprise and perhaps some guilt. This may lead to sexual dysfunction which is usually short-lived. For others, sexuality proceeds easily, naturally, and may become more fulfilling than it had been within the marriage.

CHANGES IN IDENTITY

Some of the most profound changes that occur in the bereaved are those that reflect their personal identity. For most people, spousal bereavement is likely to be the most disruptive, threatening, and challenging experience that they will face in their lives. Under these circumstances, it is not surprising that the potential for dramatic change exists. The bereaved are given the opportunity to think, feel, and behave in ways that may be new and foreign, ways that they otherwise might never have experienced.

Initially, the bereaved may experience an intense regression that Horowitz has described as the emergence of "latent negative self-images" (6). These are perceptions of self as being helpless, inadequate, incapable, childlike, or personally bankrupt. Also contributing to this state may be the loss of the "mirror" function of the spouse who has died and whose perceptions or social status may have contributed to the bereaved's sense of self. Over time, these feelings of inadequacy usually give way to more positive self-images, evolving as they do from the survivor's growing experiences of tolerating their grief, carrying on their tasks, and learning new ways of dealing with the world. The bereaved experience the development of a growing sense of strength, autonomy and independence, assertiveness, and maturity as a result of mastering their trials and tribulations.

The bereaved also go through a significant and at times radical alteration of their world view—the set of beliefs by which they operate. Following their loss, the bereaved are frequently floundering for direction, often well into the second year. This loss of direction and meaning is precipitated by the disruption of the plans and hopes they shared with their spouses, or by shattering of belief systems which governed many of their actions: beliefs in being able to control one's destiny, maintain invincibility, belief in a just and merciful God, deferred gratification, and unbounded optimism. All such beliefs are challenged, fall short, and leave a vacuum that only gradually becomes filled again—at times with modified reassertions of the old beliefs, and at times with totally new ones, reflecting the finiteness and fragility of life and the limits of control. As a result, the bereaved often become more appreciative of daily living, more patient and accepting, and more giving. They may develop new careers or change them, enjoy themselves with more gusto, or find new outlets for creativity. On the other hand, some people do stagnate or wither, unable to meet the challenges, unable to experience personal growth.

This chapter has focused on a multidimensional model of assessing clinical problems in relation to spousal bereavement. In Chapter 11, this model will be applied to the administration of therapeutic approaches to such problems.

REFERENCES

1. Lindemann E: Symptomatology and management of acute grief. Am J Psychiatry 101:141-149, 1944
2. Bowlby J: Attachment and Loss, vol. III. New York, Basic Books, 1980
3. Parkes CM: Bereavement. London, Tavistock, 1972
4. Glick IO, Parkes CM, and Weiss R: The First Year of Bereavement. New York, Basic Books, 1975
5. Clayton PJ: Mortality and morbidity in the first year of widowhood. Arch Gen Psychiatry 30:747-750, 1974
6. Horowitz M, Wilner N, Marmar C, et al: Pathological grief and the activation of latent self-images. Am J Psychiatry 137:1157-1162, 1980

Chapter 4

Adjustment to Widowhood

Sidney Zisook, M.D.
Stephen R. Shuchter, M.D.
Lucy E. Lyons

Chapter 4

Adjustment to Widowhood

Grief, the constellation of signs and symptoms following a significant loss, is generally conceptualized as a dysphoric but self-limited process (1). Yet spousal bereavement is a very disruptive and painful experience which may affect all aspects of the widowed person's life and is generally considered to be among the most stressful of life events (2). Ambivalence in the marital relationship, unanticipated loss, and a lack of social supports as well as other factors may contribute to make spousal bereavement an even more difficult and prolonged ordeal (3–5).

Since grief has been the subject of serious investigations, numerous studies have attempted to delineate normal as opposed to deviant mourning. Although the research has uncovered many aspects or areas of the bereaved's life from which outcome or recovery may be measured (3), researchers are still discovering the full range of what may be considered "normal" grief. Such a distinction may provide clinicians with the guidelines necessary for advising and counseling the bereaved as well as contributing to the knowledge base of the general public.

Because we know that the majority of those who have lost a spouse to death ultimately regain a sense of well-being and the ability to get on with their lives, it is important to track the bereavement process over long periods of time. In the early stages, we may expect, for example, to find many of the symptoms associated with depressive disorder. Depressive symptoms are ubiquitous during widowhood, and full blown depressive illnesses, occasionally leading to suicide, may also occur (6). Yet the course, prognosis, and treatment of these "depressions" are largely unknown, and their relationship to other forms of depressive disorders is still unclear.

In order to examine the full range of grief related phenomena that widows and widowers might experience, we have developed a comprehensive survey instrument for a cross-sectional study of 300 widowed persons whose spouses had died weeks to years prior to the study. This early inquiry enabled us both to test the knowledge we had gained through clinical work with the bereaved as well as to more closely examine the issues surrounding unresolved grief. One of the most important findings of this study, in fact, was that for many widowed persons the time course of grief was much more prolonged than generally expected. Although dysphoric feelings such as depression and anxiety tended to diminish over time, they did not do so to a statistically significant degree and often remained present even four or more years after the death (7).

While this investigation proved to be important, its design could allow only exploratory analysis. The generalizability of the results was limited because the sample was drawn exclusively from the San Diego Widows to Widowers Program. Furthermore, we were not able to say how the characteristics of the population or the relationship between variables had developed or would develop over time.

Our most recently completed study represents a further step in the development of a questionnaire to measure and operationalize the multiple dimensions of grief over time. Using a slightly revised version of the earlier questionnaire, 70 widows and widowers were randomly selected from public health records and were followed over a four-year period. We have previously reported the frequencies of bereavement related feelings, experiences, and behaviors across several dimensions for this population (8). We found that, generally, the most dramatic changes appeared to occur in both affective responses and items related to the survivors' continuing relationship with their dead spouses. Most Hopkins Symptoms Checklist (HSCL) subscale scores did not vary much over time, with the exception of the HSCL-Depression Scale score which was highest at one month. The Zung Depression score was also highest at one month, but did not dramatically decrease over four years.

The inability to continue working as well as before the death of their spouses was a problem for many of our subjects. Consistent with Parkes' and colleagues ongoing work, on the other hand, financial problems and medical functioning did not appear to be major difficulties for this population. Both social and sexual functioning generally improved, as most respondents found themselves able to develop new relationships as time went on. Finally, the percentage of subjects who assessed their overall adjustment to widowhood as excellent also increased with the passage of time, although a full 20 percent of the widows and widowers continued to rate their adjustment as poor to fair even after four years.

Our first report on these data provided a general portrait of our study population (8). This report represents a further expansion of that preliminary overview by identifying statistically significant differences between responses at different time periods. Additionally, this study surveys habits and behaviors, such as drinking, smoking, and drug use, that were not part of our previous reports.

METHOD

All deaths that occur in San Diego County are required to be recorded at the Department of Public Health, in the Vital Records division. Newly bereaved widows and widowers were identified by these death certificate records and were contacted by letter, with a follow-up phone call inviting them to participate in the study. No exclusion criteria were applied to the subject population, except the requirement of residence in the County. Approximately 30 percent of the widows and widowers thus contacted agreed to participate. The majority of subjects were first interviewed within three to five weeks of the death of the spouse and most first interviews were conducted in the widowed person's home.

Participants were given a semistructured interview which focused in depth on bereavement issues as well as past personal and family psychiatric history, present psychiatric symptomatology, and a Hamilton Rating Scale (the results of the semistructured personal interviews are contained in Dr. Stephen Shuchter's book *Dimensions of Grief: Adjustment to the Death of a Spouse*, 1986). In addition, the widows and widowers were asked to complete a detailed self-administered questionnaire. The design of the items contained in this questionnaire were drawn from the authors' own clinical experience with bereaved individuals, a comprehensive review of the literature, and other questionnaires used in past studies of widowhood.

Because our earlier questionnaires had contained an extensive array of questions, we were subsequently able to identify seven discrete dimensions of the bereavement process and to include the items important to these dimensions in our present study. Thus, our multidimensional widowhood questionnaire includes items related to: 1) painful affects (depression, anxiety, guilt, fear, anger); 2) coping strategies (denial, intellectualization, identification, religiosity, altruism); 3) functioning (work, social, sexual, and medical); 4) continuing relationship with the dead spouse (acceptance, identification phenomena, idealization); 5) other important relationships (family, friends, new alliances); and changes in 6) identity and self concepts as well as 7) world view. The questionnaire also contains demographic information, habits before and after the loss, classical grief-related symptoms, the Weissman Social Adjustment Scale, Holmes-Rahe Life Events Scale, Zung Depression Scale, and the 52-item version of the Hopkins Symptoms Checklist.

Following the initial interview, the widows and widowers were interviewed at three month intervals for the first two years and again at the end of the third and fourth years. In order to avoid the effects of anniversary reactions, the questionnaires were administered one month later than the three-month and yearly intervals, so that follow-up actually occurred at 4, 7, 10, 13, 16, 19, 22, 25, 37, and 49 months after the death of the spouse.

As an expansion of our early analysis, the present report continues to concentrate on yearly intervals—that is, 1 month, 13, 25, 37, and 49 months. We shall re-examine some of the variables from our preliminary report as well as include new ones. In contrast to our previous analysis, we will analyze individual change. The first graph illustrates a demographic item, while all subsequent graphs represent a dimension of the bereavement process. The percentages for each variable are plotted in the following manner: for subjects who completed the questionnaire at both month 1 and month 13 ($N = 37$); for those who completed month 13 and month 25 ($N = 39$); for those who completed month 25 and month 37 ($N = 36$); and for those who completed both months 37 and 49 ($N = 22$). To determine whether a significant change had taken place over time, each variable was dichotomized and each set of time periods was compared through the use of the McNemar Test. This procedure allowed us to use "time" as a treatment variable.

RESULTS

Seventy widows and widowers participated in the study. Sixty of the subjects were initially interviewed within one month (three to five weeks) of the death of the spouse, while 10 subjects were first interviewed at the four-month period. Approximately 60 percent of the subjects completed some questionnaires through the first three years. By the fourth year, 27 subjects (39 percent) had completed the last questionnaire.

Demographics

Forty-nine (70 percent) of the subjects were female and the mean age was 50 years, with the range from 24 to 66 years. Eleven percent of the subjects did not complete high school, 20 percent were college graduates, and 9 percent were professionals. The mean number of years the bereaved were married to the deceased spouses was 23, with a range of 2 to 39 years. The mean age of the subjects' spouses at the time of death was 52 years, with a range of 29 to 95 years. Forty-one (59 percent) of the spouses were reported to have died following a prolonged illness of longer than three months duration,

15 (21 percent) died suddenly in the absence of a prolonged illness, and the rest (20 percent) died from accidents, suicide, or other such sudden circumstances not related to illness.

Income

Figure 1 illustrates the effect of the loss on the surviving spouse's income. Prior to the death of a spouse, the average gross monthly income for this population was $1963. In the month following the death, this amount significantly decreased to about $1400. In the following three years, overall gross income rose steadily, with statistically significant increases by the end of both the first and third years. There was a slight but nonsignificant dip in income at the end of four years, perhaps due to added retirement within the population.

The effect of losing a spouse on the subsequent income of widows

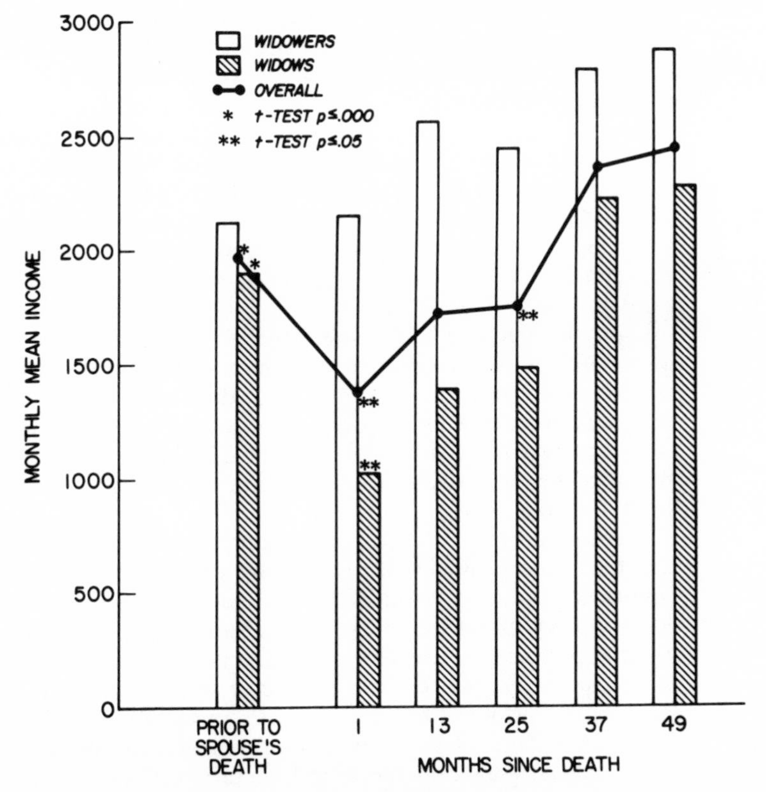

Figure 1. Mean income: overall, widowers, widows

as compared to widowers was markedly different. Prior to the loss, the difference between these groups was minimal (as the income of widows was 89 percent of that of widowers). Immediately following the death of their spouses, widowers retained 94 percent of their incomes and lost a nonsignificant 6 percent. On the other hand, the income of widows was significantly cut by 40 percent, as they retained only 60 percent of their previous incomes. Within the first year, widows' incomes significantly rose, yet they still grossed only a little over one-half—55 percent—of the income enjoyed by the widowers. In general, the income for males rose slightly and did not significantly change over the years. In contrast, the income of females was drastically reduced early on and, while it increased through the years, it never reached the amount earned by males.

Affective Responses

Figure 2 represents affective responses to the loss of the subjects' spouses. "Tearfulness" dramatically and significantly ($p = .000$) decreased between one month and the first year. Although it continues to decline in frequency, this manifestation of grief is still the most commonly experienced affective response between the first and second years of bereavement. Again, it decreased between the second and third years and appears to level off between years three and four. Of the widows and widowers who completed the questionnaire in both the third and fourth years, 14 percent at both periods of time still reported experiencing tearfulness in relation to their deceased spouses.

Approximately one-half of the subjects reported "feeling lonely" immediately after the death of their spouse. Within the first year, however, such feelings had significantly decreased ($p = .021$) and continued to decrease until the end of the second year of widowhood. The trend was complete by the end of 25 months and loneliness then remained at a relatively consistent level, about 17 percent, to the end of four years.

Although "depression" was not among the most frequent of affective responses initially, the percentage of subjects who reported this reaction only slowly diminished over time. The change in depression was very gradual, not dramatic. During the second year it is about as prevalent as tearfulness. By the end of four years, the widowed appear to have overcome their depression slightly more readily than either tearfulness or loneliness. Although not depicted in the Figure, total Zung Depression Scale scores and the Depression Scale of the HSCL paralleled the global "depression" ratings noted in Figure 2.

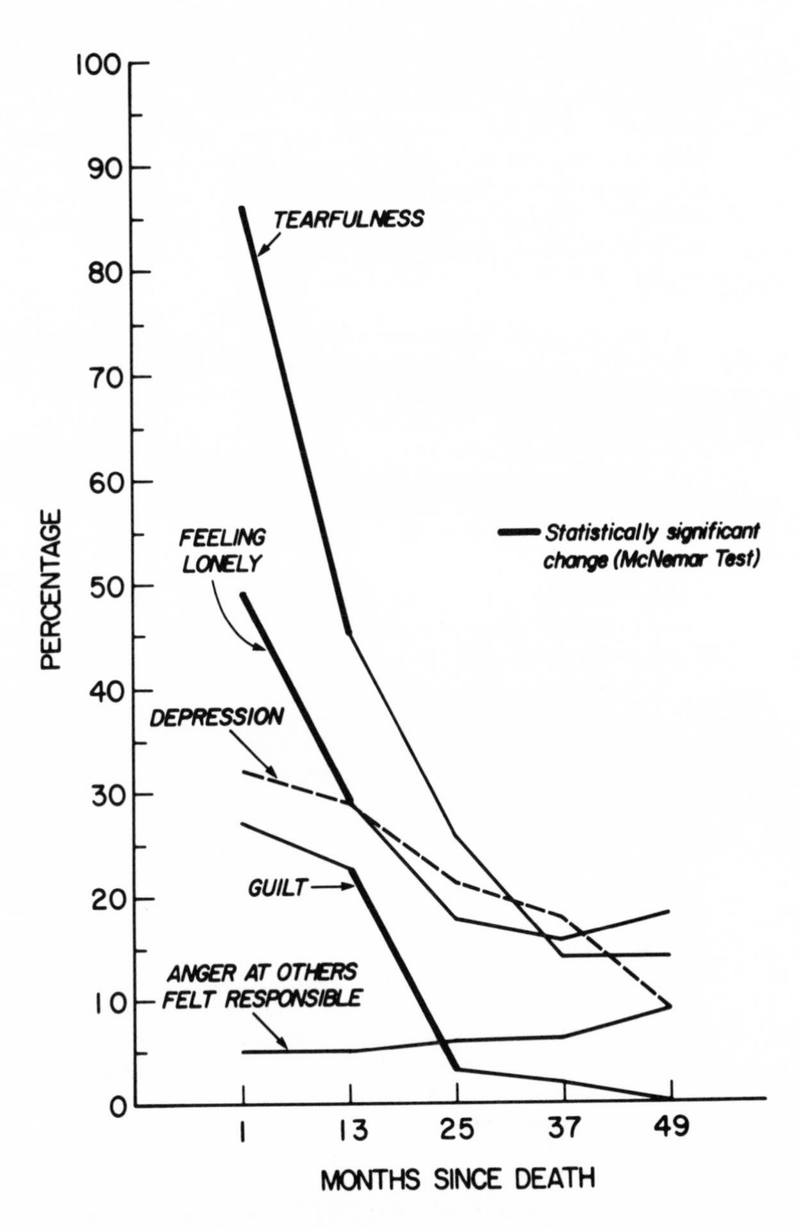

Figure 2. Affective responses

"Guilt" and "anger" were the least frequently reported initial symptoms among those displayed in Figure 2. In contrast to anger, guilt significantly decreased between the first and second years ($p = .007$) and ceased to appear between the third and fourth years. Anger at others who were felt to be in some way responsible for the spouse's death was more enduring than guilt. However, the number of subjects reporting this symptom is consistently low. Likewise, we did not find much initial response to or change in such affective symptoms as "numbness" or "apathy."

Functioning

Changes in functioning were also present, but were not as pronounced as changes in affective symptoms. Figure 3 contains three aspects of functioning: work, social/sexual, and medical. During the first year, there was a significant increase in those who felt "able to work as well as before the death" of their spouse ($p = .022$). Although there was some fluctuation, the percentages remained relatively high and the ability to work was never felt to be as impaired as it was immediately following the loss. Changes in the ability to "still enjoy sex" are most evident after the second year. There were no substantial changes in medical functioning in terms of increased illnesses. Although slight increases appear at the two- and four-year periods, the numbers are consistently too small for worthy interpretation.

Habits

Figure 4 contains an additional step in our analysis of medical functioning. For these three variables—measuring habits—we have baseline information. Subjects were asked about their alcohol intake, smoking habits, and use of medications prior to as well as following the death of their spouses. Our data do not reveal any substantial increases or decreases in alcohol use, as the levels of usage over time were consistently near to matching the baseline percentage. Nor was there any change in cigarette smoking prior to and then immediately following the loss of the spouse. Again, as in the case of alcohol, our data do not demonstrate any significant change in this habit over the long term. Finally, use of medications (over-the-counter nerve or sleeping pills, tranquilizers, sedatives, or antidepressants) increased slightly immediately following the death of a spouse and decreased markedly over each of the following three years.

Continuing Relationship with Dead Spouse

As shown in Figure 5, all of the variables related to a continuing relationship with the dead spouse decreased over time. During the

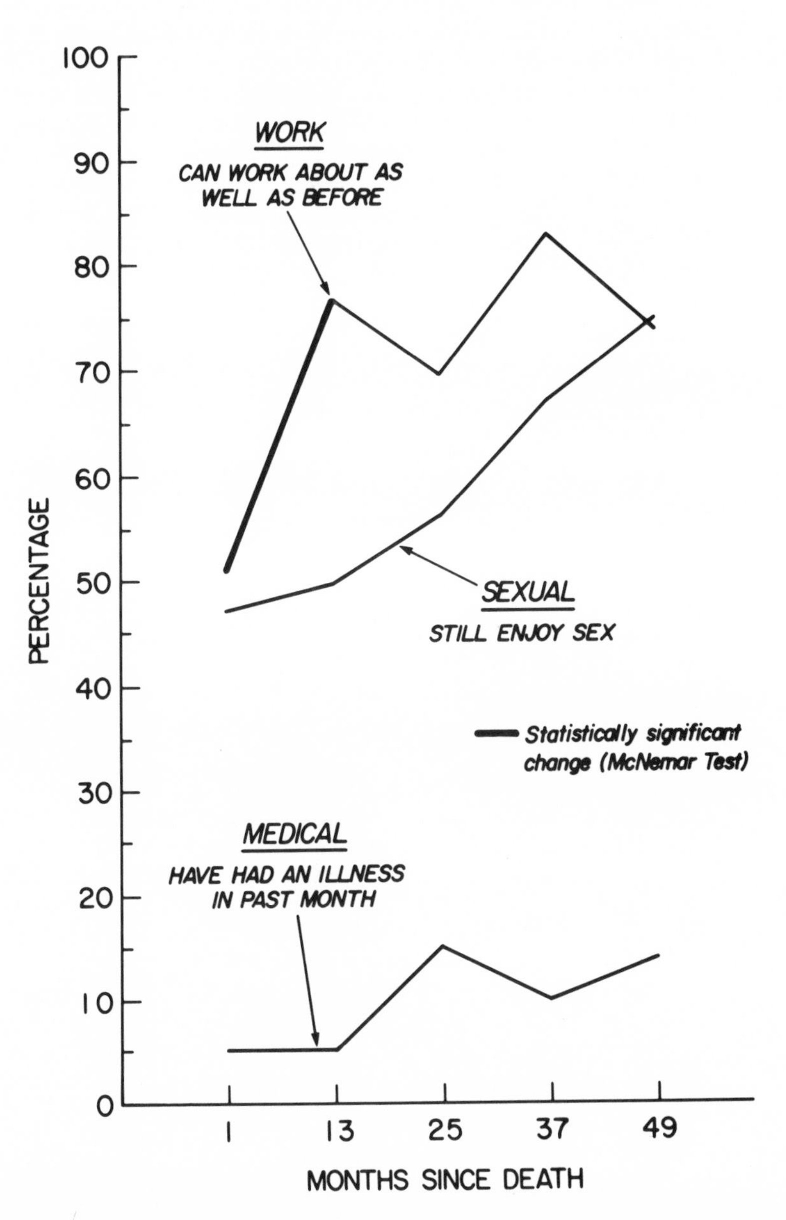

Figure 3. Functioning

first year of bereavement, there was a rapid decrease in those who experienced a "clear visual memory of the deceased spouse" (p = .002). However, by the end of two years, at least one-third of the subjects continued to have this experience and almost one-fourth of the subjects still felt this way at the end of four years. Between the onset of bereavement and one year, approximately one-half of those who had experienced "preoccupation with thoughts of the deceased" were no longer so preoccupied (p = .001). As with the maintaining of visual memories, however, it was still not uncommon at the end of four years for the bereaved to be preoccupied with thoughts of

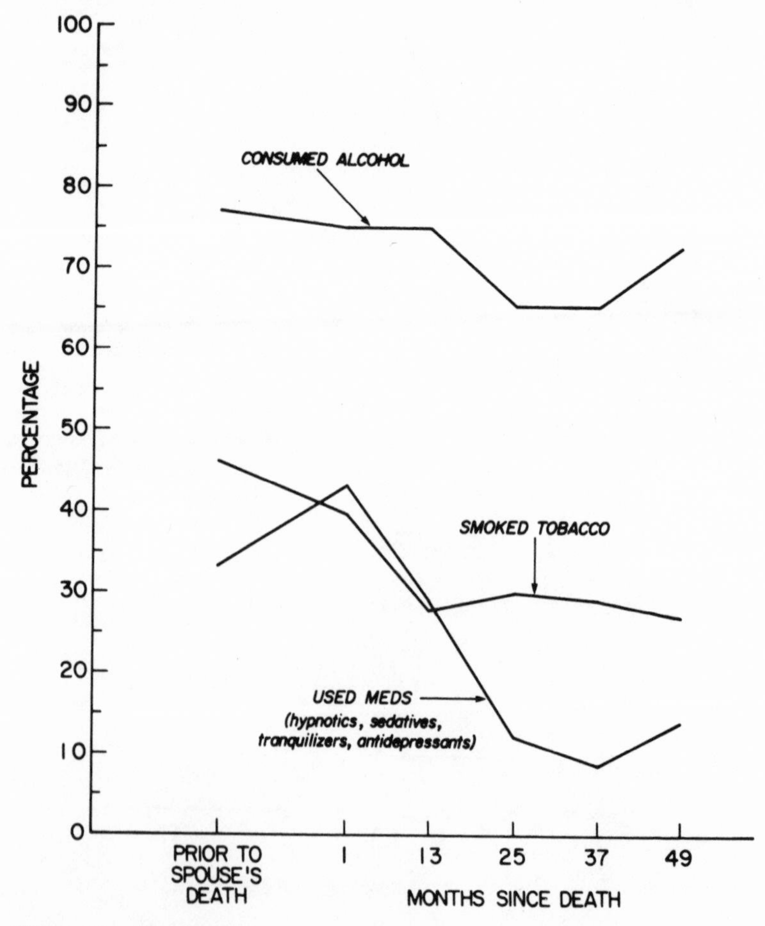

Figure 4. Habits

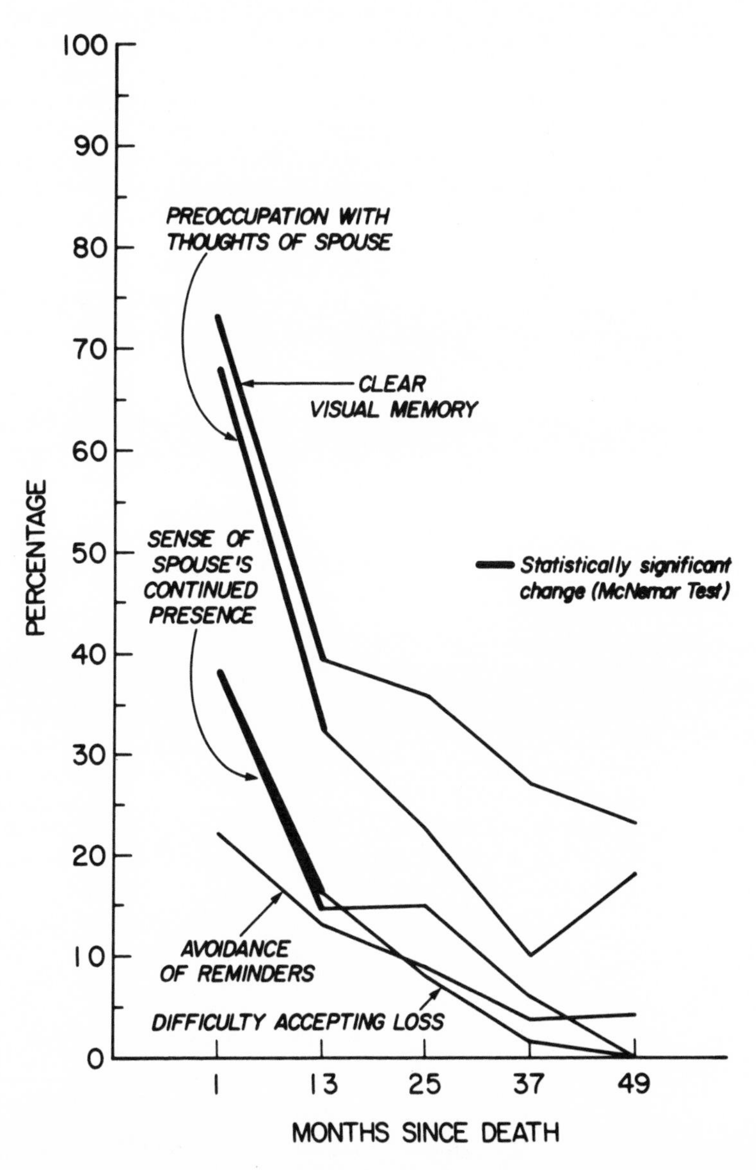

Figure 5. Continuing relationship with dead spouse

their deceased spouses. The maintaining of a continued relationship with the deceased was also evident, though less so and for a shorter period of time, in a "sense of the spouse's continued presence." After a significant decrease between onset and one year (p = .006), this sense appeared stable until the end of the second year, diminished in the third, and was absent by the fourth year. "Difficulty in accepting the loss" also significantly decreased in the first year (p = .011), and steadily subsided through the years. While approximately one-fifth of the subjects reported "avoiding reminders of the deceased" early on, there were no dramatic changes and few maintained this practice through the years.

Other Relationships

Among the variables used to measure progress in the development of other relationships were "interest in dating" and "remarriage," as represented in Figure 6. In regard to "interest in dating," a clear trend emerged as such interest increased from one month, when one-fourth of the subjects showed interest, to the end of four years, when about two-thirds expressed an interest in dating. Remarriage, as may be expected, slowly increased. Among this population, the incidence of remarriage was approximately 10 percent until between the third and fourth years of widowhood, when approximately 25 percent of the subjects had remarried.

Identity and Self-concepts

Figure 7 measures identity and self-concepts. Although the vast majority of the bereaved reported that "My life is pretty full" with little variation through the years, there was a significant change in their ability to "get as much satisfaction out of things" at the present time as compared to before the spouses' death. Between one month and one year of bereavement a statistically significant change (p = .012) occurred, leading to increased satisfaction. By the end of the fourth year, many more felt as satisfied as they used to; but the number still was not 100 percent.

Overall Adjustment

Self-rated overall "adjustment to widowhood" (Fig. 8) improved over time. Among those who rated their adjustment as excellent, the most significant change occurred between onset of bereavement and the first year (p = .015). Between the first and second years, the trend continued upward and then leveled out between the third and fourth years. Although not shown on this graph, it is important to note that by the end of the fourth year 20 percent of the widows

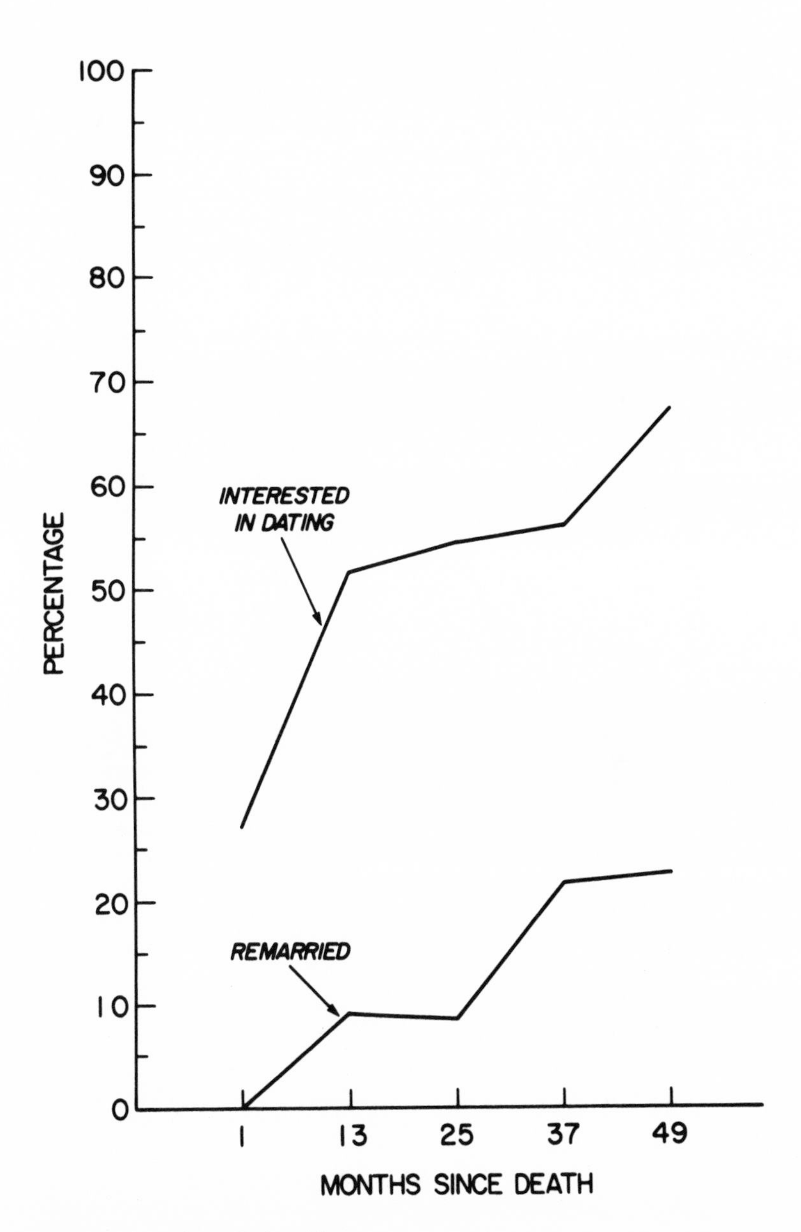

Figure 6. Other relationships

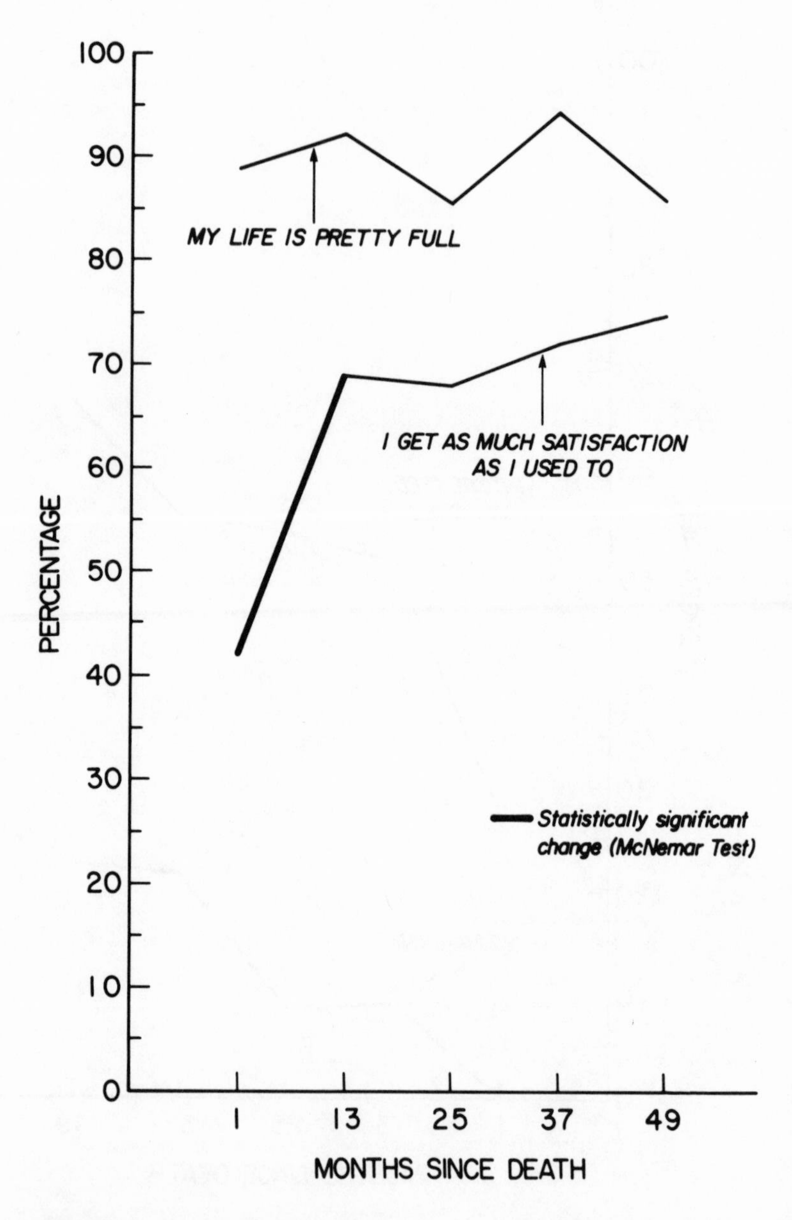

Figure 7. Identity and self-concepts

and widowers in this study rated their adjustment to widowhood as either fair or poor.

DISCUSSION

Despite the variations from individual to individual, most of those who have observed the course of grieving propose models of the grieving process which include at least three similar, partially overlapping, but distinct stages: 1) an initial period of shock, disbelief, and denial; 2) an intermediate period of acute somatic and emotional discomfort and social withdrawal; and 3) a culminating period of resolution (9–13). The time required for passage from shock through acute mourning and finally resolution of the loss varies greatly, with little agreement among various investigators regarding the time, course, and duration of "normal" bereavement. In general, the expected time course for what would be accepted as "normal" is broadening through

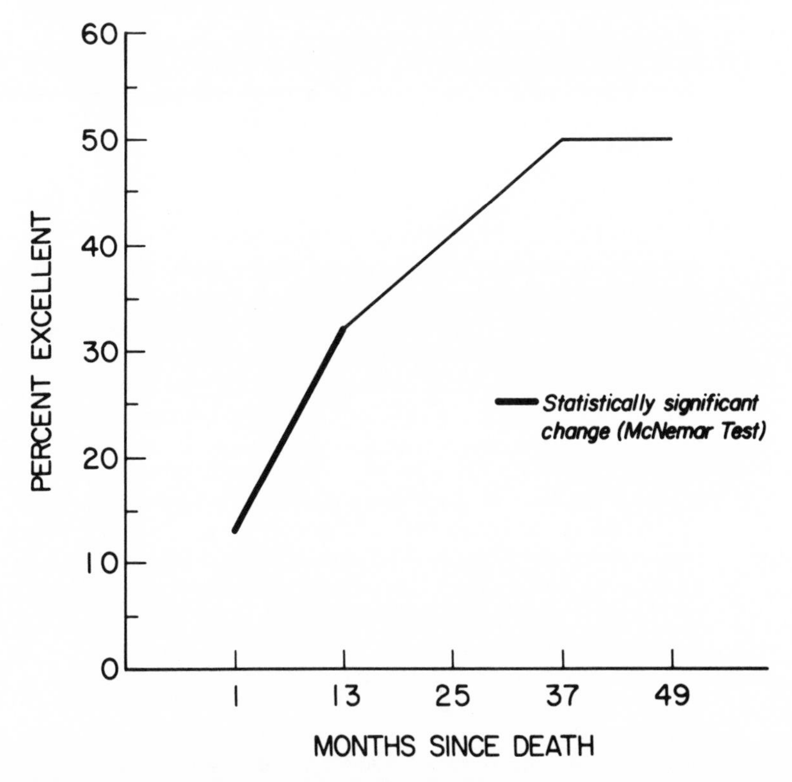

Figure 8. Overall adjustment to widowhood

the years. Lindemann, studying the symptomatology and management of acute grief, felt that the uncomplicated and undistorted grief reaction could be settled in a period of four to six weeks (11), but others have measured "normal" bereavement in months (10) or even years (14, 15).

In this study, statistically significant changes appeared most often during the first year of widowhood. During this time, there were significant decreases in the intensity and tenacity of a continuing relationship with the deceased spouse, an increase in self-satisfaction, as well as an increase in the percentage of widows and widowers who rated their adjustment to widowhood as excellent. However, there were also statistically significant changes between the first and second years of widowhood. Furthermore, there were many changes still occurring after the second year and up to the end of the fourth. Though such changes were not statistically significant (perhaps, in some cases, due to the small sample size), it is correct to say that change and trends continued even at these late periods of time. It is likely that various aspects of the bereavement process have their own unique time courses that differ from individual to individual. Thus, it seems that some aspects of grief work may take years or may never end for a certain proportion of otherwise normal bereaved individuals.

Our study, consistent with others (3, 7, 13, 16–18), found a great deal of *affective distress* during the first month of grief. Tearfulness appeared to be the most common response early on and though it significantly decreases by the first year, it remained the most prominent symptomatic response. A feeling of loneliness was experienced immediately by approximately one-half of the subjects, and then significantly decreased by the end of the first year. It is interesting to note that neither tearfulness nor loneliness completely disappeared by the end of the fourth year. On the other hand, guilt significantly decreased between the first and second years and was no longer reported by the end of the third and fourth years.

Depression, as expected, was also a frequent response at the onset of grief, yet this symptom did not decrease as rapidly as any of the aforementioned affects. It is consistent with numerous other studies (6, 13, 19) that depression was found to be relatively enduring. Anger at others who were felt to be in some way responsible for the spouse's death was never a very prominent symptom, but it was found to be quite constant over the years.

In this discussion of affective symptoms, it is also interesting to note what we did not find. Often, the first stage of grief is said to be dominated by emotional blunting and "numbness." During this period of time, which has been reported to last from hours to days, the bereaved are said to feel dazed and their functions are said to be automatic (20). In our study, we looked at both feelings of numbness and apathy. In the first month of grief, we found that approximately one-fourth of the bereaved reported feelings of numbness and approximately one-fifth reported apathy. By the end of the first year, such reports stood at only about 10 percent of the population. The change was not statistically significant in either case and neither of these affective symptoms was present by the third year. It may, indeed, be that such feelings are very short-lived and are thus not as likely to be reported as are those symptoms which persist over time. By beginning our study between weeks three and five, we might have missed much of the numbness and apathy that were already replaced by tearfulness, depression, and loneliness by one month.

One of the hallmarks of grief resolution is often considered to be the ability to return to one's work and subsequently *function* as well as before the death of the spouse (21). In our study, approximately one-half of the bereaved in the first month of grief did not feel able to work as well as before the death of their spouse. This situation significantly changed for most of the widows and widowers by the end of the first year. Although there was some fluctuation as the years passed, it is possible that such fluctuation is the normal variation within this population, as the inability to return to work is never again as low as it appeared at one month.

The ability to enjoy sex gradually increased over time. At one month, less than 50 percent of the subjects felt that they could still enjoy sex. By the end of the fourth year, approximately 75 percent of the subjects reported that their ability to enjoy sex was present.

Medical functioning, on the other hand, did not appear to be greatly affected by grief. There is still controversy over whether or not there is a significant relationship between illness onset and the death of a spouse. Many studies (3, 22, 23) have reported such a relationship. Some of the controversy may be caused by the fact that different investigators have operationalized medical functioning in different ways. We have looked at such functioning in two ways: by asking the widows and widowers if they have become worried about their health (a subjective measure), and by recording whether or not the subject was actually ill within the month of the interviews (an objective measure). We have reported (8) no demonstrated major effect on medical functioning over time as measured in the former manner, and do not now find the incidence of illness, as measured in the latter manner, to be greatly affected by grief either.

There have been numerous discussions regarding the effect that grief has on *habits* such as alcohol, tobacco, and medication usage. Most studies have reported increases in consumption of all of these immediately following the death of a loved one as well as up through the first year of bereavement. For example, in a sample of sixty-eight widows and widowers, Parkes and Brown found that 28 percent reported an increase in smoking, 28 percent reported an increase in alcohol consumption, and 26 percent had either begun to use tranquilizers or had increased their usage of the drugs 13 months following the death of the spouse (24). Maddison and Viola (25) also noted marked increases in their population of 374 widows, compared with controls, 13 months after bereavement. In addition to increased alcohol consumption and tobacco use, Maddison and Viola reported significant increases in the use of tranquilizers and sleeping pills. Thompson and colleagues (26), in a comparison of widowed versus married controls, found increases in medication use as well as new medication usage. Our data, on the other hand, do not concur with these reports.

Our findings on the use of medications were not nearly as dramatic as those reported elsewhere. In our population, there was a slight but not significant increase in medication intake immediately following as compared to before the death. However, decreased usage had already begun in the first year of widowhood and significantly decreased by the end of the second year.

We analyzed our data on alcohol and smoking habits in several ways in order to see if perhaps there were certain groups who were more vulnerable to change than others. First, we examined those who consumed any amount of alcohol versus those who abstained. There were no pronounced changes in habits from before the loss to the first month after the loss, or at any time between the subsequent years. Next, we divided the sample into 1) those who did not drink and those who drank a little (less than or equal to one drink per week) versus 2) those who drank moderately as well as heavily (see Figure 4). Again, there were no significant changes at any point. Finally, we looked at heavy drinkers (more than one drink per day) alone and did not find any substantial changes in their alcohol intake behavior. The same analytic procedures were applied to smoking habits and the same results—that is, no significant changes—were found.

Emotional acceptance can be a demanding, painful, and slow process. Goin has suggested that not only do many people maintain a "timeless" emotional involvement with the deceased, but also that this attachment often represents a healthy adaptation to the loss of a valued loved one (27). Parkes and Weiss found that, even for those men and women whose marriages were marked by problems and conflicts, the wrenching of the intense attachment bonds formed through marriage is often a long-term and difficult process (28). According to some studies, even in an uncomplicated grief reaction with a positive outcome, the constant rumination or preoccupation with thoughts of the deceased, visual memories, or a sense of the spouse's continued presence may spread over a period of the first four months or so (28). Partial denial of the loss, through disbelief, nonacceptance, and avoidance of reminders, may be an adaptive coping mechanism by helping the widowed deal with the death slowly, rather than being overwhelmed by the sudden catastrophic fact. However, even if the grieving process is going well, the bereaved never fully discontinue their relationship with the deceased spouse. They may, nonetheless, learn to function without the need to avoid such memories that early on caused distress and disruption.

In view of what we have just stated, it is not surprising that the widows and widowers in our study generally showed a very tenacious *maintenance of the relationship* with the deceased soon after the death of the spouse. The vast majority of the bereaved reported both clear visual memories of the deceased as well as a preoccupation with thoughts of the spouse. A sense of the spouse's continued presence was also evident at this time. Between one month and one year of bereavement, all three of these attachment indices significantly decreased. It should be noted, however, that in the case of the former two items, approximately one-third of the widows and widowers continued to report these between the first and second years. By the end of the fourth year, none of the bereaved still felt a sense of the spouse's continued presence, but several maintained a clear visual memory and remained preoccupied with thoughts of the deceased. This suggests that prolonged attachments are common and that for some of the widowed the deceased spouse stays with them indefinitely.

While they may be useful coping mechanisms in the early stages of grief, refusal to accept the loss and avoidance of reminders of the deceased could become problematic if present for prolonged periods of time. Avoidance, for example, may help the bereaved to get through the extremely painful initial shock of the death. However, four years later, persistent avoidance may indicate that some aspect of grief has been left unresolved. In our study, acceptance of the loss and avoidance of reminders were difficulties for only a very few widows and widowers by the end of two years. Thus, for most of the bereaved in this study, the continuation of a relationship with the deceased was more likely to take the form of attachment through visual memories or thoughts of the spouse than through avoidance of reminders or difficulty in accepting the loss. Most widows and widowers gradually learn to accept the fact of their loss, and, after a period of time, can learn to face reminders without undue pain. It is as if the survivor ultimately finds a comfortable place for the deceased, a place where memories, thoughts, and images exist but no longer overwhelm or predominate the life of the widow or widower.

Among the difficulties one encounters in bereavement research is a lack of consensus about what constitutes normal grief or a positive outcome of the bereavement process. One set of positive outcome measures, indicating substantial resolution of the social withdrawal many persons experience in the immediate aftermath of bereavement, are remarriage and the forming of *new relationships*. However, it is important to look at these items in relation to other measurements. As noted elsewhere (22), while remarriage may sometimes be a useful assessment of outcome, the fact remains that to look for a high incidence of remarriage among elderly women is unrealistic due to the lower number of available elderly men. (It is estimated that there are currently six widows for every widower in the United States) (29). Interest in dating, on the other hand, provides a clear assessment of social functioning.

In our study, interest in dating rose rapidly within the first year of bereavement and continued to increase as time progressed. By the end of four years, approximately 23 percent of the widows and widowers had remarried. Our earlier analysis showed that, in this population, the maintenance of old relationships with friends and family also proceeded well (8). Thus, for the widows and widowers in this study, the high frequency of continuance of old ties as well as the formation of new relationships appear to indicate positive outcomes. How these findings correlate with other factors of the bereavement process will be an important step in future analysis.

While other relationships were being maintained as well as developed among this population, we have simultaneously seen a high degree of affective response to the death of spouses. This phenomenon has been reported by Parkes and colleagues as well (28). It is important to recognize that all aspects of recovery from the loss of a loved one do not occur at the same rate. Therefore, widows and widowers may indeed return "to full social participation while continuing to grieve in private" (28). Very few of our subjects suffered from illnesses between the onset of grief and the first year, yet many were unable to work as well as before the death of their spouse during this same period of time. Some of our widows and widowers expressed an interest in dating, while simutaneously reporting tearfulness and feelings of loneliness.

Perhaps the above, in some way, can help to explain what otherwise looks like an inconsistency in our subjects' responses to the *identity and self-concept* items. We found that, through the end of four years, the vast majority of widows and widowers in this study consistently evaluated their lives as "pretty full." Yet, at least in the first two years, not nearly as many would have said that they were as satisfied as they used to be. Though at first glance they would appear to be quite similar, it is clear that these variables are measuring two entirely different concepts. The former may be a global assessment—that is, measuring fullness of life in terms of both good and bad experiences—while the latter is an evaluation of personal, positive satisfaction. Thus, in one sense, their lives are full, including the need to cope with widowhood. On the other hand, they are not as satisfied as they used to be, now living without their spouses. By the end of four years, however, 75 percent did feel as much satisfaction as they used to; other intervening factors may have prevented the remaining 25 percent from feeling this way by this time.

Since most widows and widowers in our study demonstrated decreasing distress and increasing satisfaction over time, it is worth asking whether they were able to truly "resolve" their grief. The difficulty in answering this question, without reservation, lies in the nature of grief. For our study, we defined the grief of widowhood as a multidimensional phenomenon. Because bereavement can affect every aspect of the widowed person's life and recovery may proceed at different rates for each different manifestation of grief, it is difficult to interpret recovery or outcome as a singular concept. However, in general, we may state that in the *resolution* of grief, the bereaved are aware of the intensity and variability of the emotions they have experienced as well as the alterations in their working and social lives. In short, they know they have grieved. Whereas in the early stages of grief attention is focused upon the deceased, in resolution, attention shifts to the world without that person. Memories are, and loneliness may be, a part of that world, but the deceased with their ills and problems are not. The mark of resolution, then, is the ability of the bereaved to recognize that they have grieved and can now return to work, resume old functions and acquire new ones as necessary, re-experience pleasure, and seek the companionship and love of others (30).

In general, we can say that the widows and widowers in our study appear to be relatively well adjusted by the end of four years. There were significant decreases in affective responses, no significant increases in illness or alcohol, tobacco, or medication consumption, and most were relatively socially active. By the end of four years, none of our subjects expressed difficulty in accepting the fact of the loss. Yet after three years there was no increase in the number of subjects who would rate their adjustment to widowhood as excellent and, of the total population, 20 percent felt that they had adjusted only fairly or poorly by the end of their fourth year of bereavement. This finding attests to the fact that the progression toward "recovery" follows a complex, painful path which has many diverse determinants. Coping with grief and its many manifestations is a long-term process, not a crisis which can be overcome in a limited time frame.

REFERENCES

1. De Vaul RA, Zisook S, Faschingbauer TR: Clinical aspects of grief and bereavement. Primary Care 6:391-402, 1979
2. Holmes TH, Rahe RH: The social readjustment rating scale. J Psychosom Res 11:213-218, 1967
3. Glick IO, Weiss RS, Parkes CM: The First Year of Bereavement. New York, Wiley Interscience, 1974
4. Maddison DC, Walker WL: Factors affecting the outcome of conjugal bereavement. Br J Psychiatry 113:1057-1067, 1967
5. Shanfield S: Predicting bereavement outcome: marital factors. Family Systems Medicine 1:40-46, 1983
6. Clayton P, Halikas JA, Maurice WL: The depression of widowhood. Br J Psychiatry 120: 71-78, 1972
7. Zisook S, Shuchter SR: Time course of spousal bereavement. Gen Hosp Psychiatry 7:95-100, 1985
8. Zisook S, Shuchter SR: The first four years of widowhood. Psychiatric Annals 16:288-298, 1986
9. Bowlby J: Processes of mourning. Int J Psychoanal 42:317, 1961
10. Engel G: Is grief a disease? Psychosom Med 23:18-23, 1961
11. Lindemann E: Symptomatology and management of acute grief. Am Journal Psychiatry 101:141-148, 1944
12. Parkes CM: Bereavement: Studies of Grief in Adult Life. New York, International Universities Press, 1972
13. Zisook S, De Vaul RA: Grief, unresolved grief and depression. Psychosomatics 24:247-256, 1983
14. Bornstein PE, Clayton PJ, Halikas JA, et al: The depression of widowhood after thirteen months. Br J Psychiatry 122:561-566, 1973
15. Parkes CM: The first year of bereavement: a longitudinal study of the reaction of London widows to the death of their husbands. Psychiatry 33:444-466, 1971
16. Zisook S, De Vaul RA, Click MA: Measuring symptoms of grief and bereavement. Am J Psychiatry 139:1550-1593, 1982
17. Zisook S, De Vaul R: Measuring acute grief. Psychiatric Medicine 2:169-176, 1984
18. Zisook S, Shuchter SR, Schuckit M: Factors in the persistence of unresolved grief among psychiatric outpatients. Psychosomatics 26:497-503, 1985

19. Lloyd C: Life events and depressive disorder reviewed, parts I and II. Arch Gen Psychiatry 37:529-535, 1980

20. Clayton PJ: The period of numbness. The Director 4-5, 1973

21. Freud S: Mourning and melancholia (1917), in Complete Psychological Works, Standard Edition, vol. 14. Translated and edited by Strachey J. London, Hogarth Press, 1961

22. Committee for the Study of Health Consequences of the Stress of Bereavement, Institute of Medicine: Bereavement: Reactions, Consequences and Care. Edited by Osterwies M, Solomon J, Green M. Washington, DC, National Academy Press, 1984

23. Klerman GL, Izen JE: The effects of bereavement and grief on physical health and well-being. Adv Psychosom Med 9:66-104, 1977

24. Parkes CM, Brown R: Health after bereavement: a controlled study of young Boston widows and widowers. Psychosom Med 34:449-461, 1972

25. Maddison DC, Viola A: The health of widows in the year following bereavement. J Psychosom Res 12:297-306, 1968

26. Thompson L, Breckenridge J, Gallagher D, et al: Effects of bereavement on self-perceptions of physical health in elderly widows and widowers. J Gerontol 39:309-314, 1984

27. Goin MK, Burgoyne RE, Goin JM: Timeless attachment to a dead relative. Am J Psychiatry 136:988-989, 1979

28. Parkes CM, Weiss RS: Recovery from Bereavement. New York, Basic Books, 1983

29. Collins, Glen: Helping widows to cope. New York Times, April 7, 1986

30. Zisook S, DeVaul R: Unresolved grief. Am J Psychoanal 45:370-379, 1985

Chapter 5

Psychological Adjustment to Unnatural Dying

Edward K. Rynearson, M.D.

Chapter 5

Psychological Adjustment to Unnatural Dying

If your mind is like mine, it tends to shrink when focused on a concept as vast as dying. And when invited to consider unnatural death, your mind might recoil, as well. Before reciting numbers and definitions, I will present several real experiences:

An 18-year-old homecoming princess is crushed in her boyfriend's overturned car while driving home from a kegger.

A psychiatrist with rapidly advancing multiple sclerosis waits until he is dysarthric before killing himself with an overdose.

An 80-year-old man shoots his wife to save her from the indignity of her deterioration with Alzheimer's disease.

A young schizophrenic mother sacrifices her two children by drowning them to quiet the hallucinated demands of Christ.

A psychopathic serial killer rapes, strangles, and buries 27 women.

An uneducated black laborer, enraged by his inability to find work, shoots his wife in a drunken fury.

Four hundred and ninety-one celebrating people burn and suffocate to death in the Coconut Grove Nightclub fire.

These vignettes describe actual cases. My purpose is to introduce the dissonance and complexity of unnatural dying. Each of these abbreviated descriptions presents a unique drama of unnatural dying whose form and forces distinguish it from natural dying. Natural dying follows diseases or inevitable deteriorations that are to some degree anticipated and acceptable. Unnatural dying follows accidents, suicides, or homicides that are characterized by horror, brutality, and calamity—abhorrent acts that are psychosocially dissonant and to some degree unacceptable.

Unnatural dying presents at least three phenomenologic peculiarities of dying:

1. *Violence*—The act of dying is injurious.
2. *Violation*—the act of dying is transgressive.
3. *Volition*—The act of dying is a willful intention (suicide and homicide) or an irresponsible negligence (most accidents are secondary to human error rather than natural disasters).

These three Vs of unnatural dying (violence, violation, and volition) are far from inert or neutral phenomena. Each of them catalyzes a strong psychosocial aftermath. When the dying is unnatural, subsequent clinical reactions of friends and relatives must contain and conform to these discordant rudiments. This is so obvious—the peaceful dying of someone ringed by nurturing relatives is categorically distinct from the brutal dying of someone who is stabbed repeatedly by an assaultive thief or someone who is hit in a crosswalk by a drunk driver, or someone who is partially decapitated by a self-inflicted gunshot wound. It is the form and context of dying rather than death itself that lends meaning and structure to the psychologic recapitulation and assimilation of death by the bereaved. Death itself is followed by bereavement or its pathologic forms; unnatural dying demands not only normal and/or pathologic bereavement, but adjustment to a death that is to some degree characterized by violence, violation, and volition.

This chapter will describe the syndromal affects that are specifically associated with unnatural dying. Tentative explanatory models will be developed that will serve as a basis for therapeutic approach. Finally, these tentative models might offer prediction of future morbidity, which would be of relevance to both clinician and researcher.

THE COCONUT GROVE FIRE REVISITED

This tragedy inaugurated the first outcome study of bereavement and its effects. While the survivors and relatives of victims of this tragedy were forced to adjust to unnatural rather than natural dying, this distinction (and its independent effects upon bereavement) has not been widely appreciated. In fairness to the original researchers, this error of nondifferentiation may have been magnified by subsequent authors. When have you read a study on bereavement that failed to cite the Coconut Grove disaster research as validating the genesis and course of normal and abnormal bereavement? This assigns an ordination of truth to a referent that made no such claim. A review of the original studies will illustrate that their claims were speculative and tentative.

In November 1942, the Coconut Grove Nightclub in Boston incinerated nearly 500 people within an hour's time. They were dispersed to various hospitals in Boston, including Massachusetts General and Boston City Hospital. The neuropsychiatric department of each hospital launched independent studies of the psychological effects of the disaster. While the investigators (Lindemann at Massachusetts General and Adler at Boston City Hospital) were assessing subjects who were adjusting to the same event, their divergent analyses were based upon dissimilar models.

Lindemann's Model

In September 1943, Lindemann reported his "neuropyschiatric observations" of the Coconut Grove survivors (1). He studied 32 subjects and reported that 14 initially presented with neuropsychiatric problems, but there was no systematic follow-up to monitor outcome. Seven of the survivors had lost a relative in the fire. Their presentation and management were the major objectives of the paper. One of Lindemann's case presentations illustrates the development of his conceptual model:

> A young man had received only minor burns and left the hospital apparently well on the road to recovery just before the psychiatric survey took place. On the fifth day, he learned that his wife had died. He seemed somewhat relieved of his worry about her fate, and impressed the surgeon as being unusually well controlled during the short period of his stay in the hospital that followed. There seemed to be no occasion for any psychiatric attention.
>
> On January 1, 1943, he was returned to the hospital by his family. He complained about his feelings of extreme tension, inability to breathe, generalized weakness and exhaustion, and his frantic fear that some terrible thing was going to happen. "I'm destined to live in insanity or I must die, I know that is God's will. I have this awful feeling of guilt." With intense morbid guilt feelings, he reviewed incessantly the events of the fire. His wife had stayed behind. When he tried to pull her out, he had fainted and was shoved out by the crowd. She was burned while he was saved. "I should have saved her or I should have died too." He complained about being filled with an incredible violence and did not know what to do about it. The rapport that could be established with him lasted for only brief periods of time. He then would fall back into his state of intense agitation and muttering. He slept poorly, even with heavy sedation. In the course of four days he became somewhat more composed, had longer periods of contact with the psychiatrist, and seemed to feel that he was being understood and might be able to cope with his

> morbid feelings of guilt and violent impulses. On the sixth day of his hospital stay, however, after skillfully distracting the attention of his special nurse, he jumped through a closed window to a violent death.

Lindemann focused on the issue of distorted grief, which he considered to be secondary to unconscious conflict. He interpreted the subject's prolonged and intense symptoms of anxiety, intrusive recollections of the fire, and compensatory numbing as manifestations of pathologic grief—an autoplastic reflection of underlying ambivalence. He retrospectively proposed that this complicated decathexis had been preceded by a relationship characterized by conflict and suppressed hostility when he said, "The more severe emotional disturbance encountered in formerly well adjusted patients seems to be due not so much to the impersonal effects of the disaster (fright and horror) as to the problems in personal and social relationships involving conflict and guilt" (1, p. 823).

In September 1944, Lindemann's widely quoted paper, "Symptomatology and Management of Acute Grief," appeared (2). The author further developed and elaborated the themes from his previous paper based upon observations of additional subjects acutely bereaved by natural dying and war casualties. While the final cohort consisted of 101 subjects, he did not differentiate between those bereaved as a result of natural or unnatural causes of death. Lindemann considered death to be a generic event. He cogently described bereavement responses and differentiated atypical forms of grief, but overlooked the effects specifically associated with either natural or unnatural dying. This model similarly narrowed therapeutic objectives to the uncovering and assimilation of ambivalence. This derived from the brilliant speculations of Freud, but Lindemann's inaccurately and inordinately quoted study transformed that speculation into a fundamental supposition of bereavement treatment and research. While this model may have validity as a contributant to atypical forms of grief, its overinclusive application may result in misinterpreted theory and misleading treatment. Lindemann's later study of bereavement after suicide noted his awareness of this difference (3).

Adler's Model

Adler noted the same commonality of anxiety and intrusive recollections, recurring nightmares, and compensatory numbing in her subjects (4). She followed a cohort (*N* = 46 subjects) for one year and reported that 20 percent continued to experience disabling symptoms. While citing bereavement as a variable, she established that only one-half of the subjects who developed disabling symptoms after one year had lost a relative. Another intriguing finding was that unconsciousness was a moderating variable. Unconsciousness was a common occurrence to survivors exposed to intense fumes; if the interval of unconsciousness was longer than one hour, their retrograde amnesia prevented posttraumatic psychologic reactions.

This model of overwhelming external trauma resulting in a "fear neurosis" as differentiated from a "conflict neurosis" was based upon the findings of Symonds (5), Kardiner (6), and others who had worked with psychiatrically disabled war veterans. One of her case presentations contains features nearly identical with Lindemann's and illustrates that her posttraumatic model is more inclusive of the specific events of unnatural dying:

> A youth of 20, a clerk, had been somewhat excitable and easily angered prior to his injury. Aside from that he had been well adjusted in his professional and married life. On the night of the disaster he was about to leave the nightclub and stood near an exit waiting for his wife, who was four months pregnant. He suddenly saw flames, was milled around, lost sight of his wife, and soon escaped through an exit. The patient suffered second degree burns of the face, neck and hands. Five percent of the total skin area was involved. Shortly before leaving the hospital on December 15, 1942, he was told by the priest that his wife had perished in the fire. Until then he had thought she had been saved. He became deeply depressed and has been so ever since. He went back to work in January of 1943, but his working capacity has suffered. He is much slower and has lost all interest in his work. In his spare time he thinks of the disaster and of his wife, feels that he will never be interested in another girl. He cannot concentrate and starts shaking all over whenever he has a slight argument. He is constantly afraid of another fire, would never dare to go to a nightclub again. He sits down at moving pictures only if there is a seat in the last row so that he can get out quickly. He takes the same precautions in dining rooms. The sound of fire engines awakens him at night with a start. He had had no nightmares in the hospital, but they began one week after he came home. In the following months he relived the scenes of the fire in five terrifying dreams. They still occur, though rarely (4, p. 1100).[1]

Adler's model is more intensely focused on the external traumatic events and their psychologic assimilation rather than on the presumption of internal, unconscious trauma and decathexis. What little attention she gives to treatment alludes to measures that provide support, education, rest, and sedation.

I have often wondered why these researchers failed to collaborate.

---

[1]Reprinted from JAMA 123:1100, 1943. Copyright 1943, American Medical Association. Reprinted by permission.

There were some overtures, but apparently the issue of territoriality and pressure for independent publication would not allow a shared research design and report (A. Adler, personal communication). Presumably a more inclusive and better validated study would have resulted. Furthermore, the psychologic effects of unnatural dying would have been clarified, as they have been with subsequent clinical research with bereaved survivors of catastrophic fires (7).

A PROPOSAL FOR A CONCEPTUAL FRAMEWORK

These preliminary findings of the effects of unnatural dying have been further delineated and illuminated by subsequent clinical research. This has led to some new ideas on the organizing principles underlying the adjustment to unnatural dying. While the following outline is speculative and may be incorrect in some of its detail, the theme is rich enough in its clinical and theoretical potential to warrant consideration. I shall introduce these principles as propositions and briefly develop a conceptual model for each.

Proposition 1

The adjustment to unnatural death involves a variable combination of violence, violation, and volition. Homicidal, suicidal, and accidental dying involve violence, violation, and volition in a characteristic pattern (see Table 1). These three forms of unnatural dying follow a relative hierarchy (homicide, suicide, accident) in the presence of the three distinguishing variables. Presumably the adjustive challenge of homicidal, suicidal, and accidental dying would follow this same order of succession if the effects were additive.

Proposition 2

The adjustment to an unnatural death is a complex state that dynamically controls in a self-regulatory manner the ratio of acceptance and denial of these dissonant variables of violence, violation, and volition. Each of the variables is associated with a compensatory psychologic response: violence with posttraumatic stress, violation with victimization, and volition with compulsive inquiry.

Violence as an unanticipated, lethal, injurious act qualifies as a stressor "that would evoke significant symptoms of distress in almost everyone" as defined by the *Diagnostic and Statistical Manual of Mental Disorders, Third Edition* (*DSM-III*) (8). The model of ***posttraumatic stress*** accurately encompasses the reaction to violence; that is, psychologic reactions to trauma consisting of hyperreactivity (startle reactions, explosive outbursts of anger) and recurrent, intrusive recollections of the trauma (flashbacks, nightmares) alternating with a compensatory psychic numbing, constriction of affect, social functioning, and loss of sense of control over one's destiny (9). Descriptive studies of survivors or relatives of accidental (10–17), suicidal (18), or homicidal (19) victims have established a strong association of violence and posttraumatic stress phenomena.

Violation as an unprovoked, transgressive, exploitative act is followed by the psychologic reaction of *victimization*. The model of victimization was recently described by Ochberg, who proposed a clinical definition: "The core concept and definition of victimization is a physical assault or threat of assault in which physical damage or violation occurs, accompanied by a sense on the part of the victim of reduction in dominance and concomitant resignation or rage or both. Victimization is, therefore, a complex concept involving an assailant, an interaction, a victim, and a set of biological, psychological, and interpersonal sequelae that are inevitably experienced by the victim as a traumatic departure from a state of equilibrium" (20, p. 13).

In his most recent work, Ochberg has proposed a list of symptoms as descriptive criteria for victimization (21):

A. *Shame:* deep embarrassment, often characterized as humiliation or mortification
B. *Self-blame:* exaggerated feelings of responsibility for the traumatic event, with guilt and remorse, despite obvious evidence of innocence
C. *Subjugation:* feeling belittled, dehumanized, lowered in dominance, powerless, as a direct result of the trauma
D. *Morbid hatred:* obsessions of vengeance and preoccupation with hurting or humiliating the perpetrator with or without outbursts of anger or rage
E. *Defilement:* feeling dirty, disgusted, disgusting, tainted, "like spoiled goods," and in extreme cases, rotten and evil
F. *Resignation:* a state of broken will or despair, often associated with repetitive victimization or prolonged exploitation with markedly diminished interest in past or future

Posttraumatic stress may be viewed as a physiologic reaction preventing or preparing for further violence; victimization is the psychologic counterpart, providing an identification that protects a self-identity compromised by helplessness and hopelessness. Symptoms of victimization have been noted in survivors of homicidal (22–24) and accidental dying (25–28). They have not been reported following

Table 1. Responses to Unnatural Dying

	Violence		Volition	Violation
Homicide	*Intense*		*Intense*	*Intense*
	Firearm	64%		
	Stabbing	19%	Other as agent	Criminal homicide
	Clubbing	11%		
	Beating	6%		
	Total	100% *1981		
Suicide	*Intense*		*Intense*	*Absent*
	Firearm	58%		
	Poison	20%	Self as agent	
	Hanging	14%		
	Other	8%		
	Total	100% **1981		

Accident	*Intense*			*Weak*	*Moderate*
	Motor vehicle	51%		Human negligence or recklessness	Negligent homicide or misdemeanor
	Falls	13%			
	Fires	6%			
	Drowing	5%		*Absent*	
	Choking	3%			
	Poisoning	3%		Random occurrence	
	Airplane	2%			
	Other	17%			
	Total	100%	***1981		

* Report to the Nation on Crime and Justice, U.S. Bureau of Statistics, NCJ–87068, p14, Oct 1983
** Statistical Abstracts of the U.S., Bureau of the Census, 105th edition, p79, 1985
***Statistical Abstracts of the U.S., Bureau of the Census, 105th edition, p78, 1985

suicide, presumably because violation is not strongly associated with this form of unnatural death.

Volition as an act of willful, intentional killing (homicide and suicide) or as an irresponsible negligence leading to death (accidental death is usually a product of human error) is followed by a ***compulsive inquiry*** to establish the locus of responsibility and the purpose of the death, if it was intended. While this inquiry initially may be assumed by an external investigative judicial agency, the survivor carries out an internal, private inquiry that will continue long after external definition. The model of compulsive inquiry is applicable in those situations in which our minds are confronted by existential dilemmas or dichotomies that are inherently unresolvable (29). To create an acceptable explanation of killing is a mandatory inquest, but it only promises further uncertainties and ambiguities. The problem of putting some frame of meaning around something so irrational is insurmountable.

Compulsive inquiry is intensified when a perpetrator is not found after a homicide or accidental death. The external definition of the perpetrator's motive and/or negligence provides more coherence and comprehension of the abhorrent act. Lacking such external definition, the survivor is left with lingering doubts, questions, and fears.

Survivors of those who have died by suicide are particularly stymied in their inquiries (30), for suicide is an act of choice. The victim is the perpetrator. There is no crime to solve and no one to punish, leaving the survivor alone to face the dilemma.

This syndromal combination of posttraumatic stress, victimization, and compulsive inquiry is specifically associated with the variables of unnatural dying and occurs independent of antecedent psychopathology or an ambivalent relationship with the deceased. Presumably, certain antecedent psychologic conditions might render survivors more vulnerable; that is, phobic disorders to posttraumatic stress, paranoid disorders to victimization, or obsessive disorders to compulsive inquiry. However, it would be erroneous to attempt validation of this association with a retrospective study. While antecedent and direct variables may mutually influence adjustment, it would be misleading to postulate (as Lindemann did from Freud's speculation) that posttraumatic stress, victimization, and compulsive inquiry are reflections of unconscious conflict. Rather, they appear to be the psychologic consequences of overwhelming affect and defensive collapse.

Proposition 3

The adjustment to an unnatural death is positively correlated with the degree of identification with the victim. This identification is substantiated by the common occurrence of the syndromal reactions in the absence of direct exposure to the unnatural death. It is rare that the actual death is witnessed, but the mechanism of identification demands a paradoxical recapitulation and adjustment to violence, violation, and volition for the survivor rather than for the victim.

Proposition 4

The adjustment to an unnatural death must include the sociocultural consequences of transgressive violence, violation, and volition. The sympathy and sociocultural support extended in cases of natural death evaporate in cases of unnatural death. The survivor of an attempted homicide or suicide becomes the focus of widespread publicity and intense investigation. This may be followed by the process of trial and punishment. Unnatural death is so abhorrent and stigmatizing that the survivors report themselves to be isolated and avoided by others. This sociocultural compulsion to establish blame and retribution while avoiding the acceptance of death handicap a survivor's adjustment. Paradoxically, the responses of posttraumatic stress, victimization, and compulsive inquiry may be augmented by these sociocultural responses.

RECOVERY AND TREATMENT IMPLICATIONS

Let us consider an actual case to test the relevance of these propositions:

> It was the recurring dream of his daughter's murder that forced this man into treatment. He couldn't bear to sleep. The same horrific dream awaited him, and his dread of the dream transformed sleep into an ordeal. He would thrash about in bed feeling besieged, grimly walling himself off from his unconscious. He had not witnessed his daughter's murder, but in the dream he was transfixed as a mute observer. She was walking from a bus stop to school when a man rushed up and then dragged her into a car. Bound and gagged, she was driven to an isolated house. She was raped, beaten, and branded with cigarettes. Each of these ghastly acts followed an inexorable sequence while he watched in panic. The dream would end as her throat was being cut, and he would awaken gasping and screaming.
>
> In the year since her murder, these were this man's enduring images of his dead daughter. The horror of her death seemed to eclipse her warmth. Her death had isolated him from surrounding life. He felt paralyzed in his remaining relationships, distrusting his capacity and need for nurturance. He was enraged at the detectives who had never found the killer and at the court system that seemed more concerned with legal technicalities than with justice. He blamed himself for her death, and

caring for others now included only the immediate members of his family, over whom he kept a grim vigil.

When the images began to emerge during the day, he was unable to contain his panic or concentrate at work. He knew that he needed help, but he could not anticipate improvement. The enveloping bereavement was so absolute in its hopelessness that it transformed the future into something empty and futile.

As his therapist, I too felt traumatized and futile. I found myself so shaken by these traumatic descriptions of dying that after each session I felt apprehensive and exhausted and, like my patient, had unbidden "flashbacks" of the death. I would sometimes dread future sessions, obligated to observe an event that neither of us had actually witnessed.

Proposition 1 would predict that our patient's adjustment to homicidal dying would invoke the enforced acceptance of all three variables of unnatural dying. It is noteworthy that the therapist is placed in the same psychologic position regarding these unnatural factors. In this instance the therapy situation comprehends violence, violation, and volition as tangible external events as well as fantasied or unconsious integrals. Proposition 1 would suggest that adjustment to homicidal dying might be complicated and prolonged by the presence of all three variables of unnatural dying. Clinical reports have substantiated that spontaneous adjustment to homicidal dying takes years rather than months (31, 32).

Proposition 2 would predict that our patient's adjustment would not only involve the fundamental reaction of bereavement, but would also involve a constellation of clinical findings (posttraumatic stress, victimization, and compulsive inquiry) that are directly related to unnatural dying. Since these clinical sequelae of unnatural dying last for years, they might be misinterpreted as reflections of pathologic grief. This misdiagnosis might misdirect our conceptual and therapeutic approach to search for unconscious psychologic conflicts. The conceptual model of unnatural dying presented here would suggest that our patient's psychological defenses had been overwhelmed by painful affects generated by his daughter's gruesome dying—a condition of defensive collapse rather than defensive conflict. It is important for the clinician to differentiate the dynamic concept of adult catastrophic reaction from the more fundamental and familiar concepts of infantile psychic trauma. Such a differentiation would suggest that our patient would benefit from supportive psychotherapy aimed at education, reassurance, and ventilation to enhance self-esteem and diminish painful affects. Antianxiety medication and cognitive anxiety management techniques have also been recommended. Treatment strategies for patients with posttraumatic stress, victimization, and compulsive inquiry share in this supportive, active, eclectic orientation (33, 34). However, this area of psychotherapy research lacks controlled, prospective study.

Proposition 3 would predict that our patient's adjustive dilemma is correlated with the intense degree of identification with his daughter. This model of identificatory reenactment of unnatural dying allows a working perspective for both patient and therapist. The therapist may offer personal reactions of posttraumatic stress, victimization, and compulsive inquiry toward the unnatural dying as they occur during treatment to validate the "normality" of these responses. The identificatory model allows the adjustment to be viewed as normative and purposeful. This identificatory model would also suggest that support groups composed of other survivors of people who have died unnatural deaths would offer a shared awareness more immediate and practical than that of most clinicians.

Proposition 4 would predict that our patient's adjustment to his daughter's unnatural dying would demand his involvement in the investigation, trial, and punishment of the murderer. Homicide demands a more vigorous inquest and retribution than accidental or suicidal death, but in any case the investigative and judicial diversion promises more than it can provide. Survivors are often disillusioned and sometimes enraged by their frustrated belief that justice will be served by a ritual that promises punishment and redemption.

Compulsive involvement in solution and punishment of the person who caused the unnatural death may serve the defensive purpose of displacement. This compulsion, once recognized, will be interpreted as a resistance to the acceptance of painful, repressed bereavement.

Therapy will provide an opportunity for ventilation of responses to unnatural dying that are unwelcomed by most (if not all) of those who provide emotional support for the survivor. Once initiated, the survivor feels an inordinate need to review in detail the reconstruction of the unnatural dying. The terminal experience of the victim is reenacted—sometimes repeatedly—in an apparent effort to master and objectify such an alien and terrifying occurrence.

IMPLICATIONS FOR THE CLINICIAN

Unnatural deaths account for 152,000 or 8 percent of deaths annually in the United States (35). Accidental death is twice as common as suicide or homicide. It should be noted that these three types of death are the leading cause of death from birth until the fourth decade (36). Because unnatural death most commonly touches the lives of relatively young parents and children, the clinician who treats children and/or families should be sensitive to the common factors involved in this form of death and bereavement.

IMPLICATIONS FOR THE RESEARCHER

There is considerable clinical evidence to support the premise that unnatural dying directly influences the nature and course of bereavement. The intense and prolonged syndromal effects of unnatural dying appear to be of predictive reliability (37). Subjects whose bereavement is associated with unnatural dying should be treated as a separate research population. Our model would predict a greater incidence of symptoms of posttraumatic stress, victimization, and compulsive inquiry in subjects adjusting to unnatural versus natural dying. Homicidal, suicidal, and accidental dying would independently induce those effects in descending order of correlation.

EPILOGUE

This chapter began by expressing the hope that it would stimulate and expand further thought. The task of ordering clinical phenomena and suggesting explanations, while necessarily reductive, is not meant to be restrictive. The best I can do is to lead you through my own way of viewing this painful and confusing odyssey that begins after an unnatural death so that you can share my bewilderment, so that the same doubts can arise for you as they arose for me, so that you can attempt a solution along with me. The inherent dilemma of phenomenologic inquiry is to understand what cannot be known. I do not pretend to know a unitary truth about unnatural death—only a different way of understanding it.

REFERENCES

1. Cobb S, Lindemann E: Neuropsychiatric observations. Ann Surg 117:814-824, 1943
2. Lindemann E: Symptomology and management of acute grief. Am J Psychiatry 101:141-148, 1944
3. Lindemann E, Greer IM: A study of grief: emotional responses to suicide, in Survivors of Suicide. Edited by Cain AC. Springfield, Ill, Charles C Thomas, 1972
4. Adler A: Neuropsychiatric complications in victims of Boston's Coconut Grove disaster. JAMA 123:1098-1101, 1943
5. Symonds CP: Anxiety neurosis in combatants. Lancet 245:785-789, 1943
6. Kardiner A: The Traumatic Neuroses of War. New York, Paul B. Hoeber, 1941
7. Greene BL, Grace M, Lindy J, et al: Levels of functional impairment following a civilian disaster: the Beverly Hills Supper Club fire. J Consult Clin Psychol 51:573-580, 1983
8. Spitzer R (Ed): Diagnostic and Statistical Manual of Mental Disorders, Third Edition. Washington DC, American Psychiatric Association, 1980
9. van der Kolk BA: Posttraumatic stress disorder: psychological and biological sequelae. Washington, DC, American Psychiatric Press, Inc., 1984
10. Adler A. Two different types of post-traumatic neuroses. Am J Psychiatry 102:237-240, 1945
11. Friedman P, Linn L: Some psychiatric notes on the Andrea Doria disaster. Am J Psychiatry 114:426-432, 1957
12. Leopold RL, Dillon H: Psycho-anatomy of a disaster: a long-term study of post-traumatic neuroses in survivors of a marine explosion. Am J Psychiatry 119:913-921, 1963
13. Hobert A, McCaughey BG: The traumatic effects of collision at sea. Am J Psychiatry 141:70-73, 1984
14. Wilkinson CB: Aftermath of a disaster: the collapse of the Hyatt Regency Hotel skywalks. Am J Psychiatry 140:1134-1139, 1983
15. Adams PR, Adams GR: Mount Saint Helen's ashfall: evidence for a disaster stress reaction. Am Psychol 39:252-260, 1984
16. McFarlane AC, Raphael B: Ash Wednesday: the effects of a bushfire. Aust NZ J Psychiatry 18:341-351, 1984

17. McFarlane AC: The effects of stressful life events and disasters: research and theoretical issues. Aust NZ J Psychiatry 19:409-421, 1985

18. Sheskin A, Wallace S: Differing bereavements: suicide, natural, and accidental death. Omega 7:229-242, 1976

19. Rynearson EK: Bereavement after homicide: a descriptive study. Am J Psychiatry 141:1452-1454, 1984

20. Ochberg FM, Fojtik KM: A comprehensive mental health clinical service program for victims: clinical issues and therapeutic strategies. American Journal of Social Psychiatry 4:12-23, 1984

21. Ochberg FM: Posttraumatic Therapy With the Victim of Violence. New York, Brunner/Mazel, 1986

22. Burgess A: Family reaction to homicide. Am J Orthopsychiatry 45:391-398, 1975

23. Getzel G: Serving families who survive homicide victims: social casework. Journal of Contemporary Social Work 65:138-144, 1985

24. Rynearson EK: The homicide of a child, in: Posttraumatic Therapy With the Victim of Violence. Edited by Ochberg FM. New York, Brunner/Mazel, 1986

25. Beigel A, Berren MR: Human-induced disasters. Psychiatric Annals 15:143-150, 1985

26. Krupnick J, Horowitz M: Victims of violence: psychological responses, treatment implications. Evaluation and Change (special issue):42-46, 1980

27. Kinston W, Rosser R: Disaster: effects on mental and physical states. J Psychosom Res 18:437-456, 1974

28. Frederick C: Effects of natural vs. human induced violence upon victims. Evaluation and Change (special issue):71-75, 1980

29. Fromme E: Man for Himself. Greenwich, Conn, Fawcett Publications, 1947

30. Rynearson EK: Suicide internalized: an existential sequestrum. Am J Psychiatry 138:84-87, 1981

31. Knapp RJ: The murdered child, in Beyond Endurance: When a Child Dies. New York, Schocken Books, 1986

32. Eth S, Roberts SP: Developmental perspective on psychic trauma in childhood, in Trauma and Its Wake. Edited by Figley C. New York, Brunner/Mazel, 1985

33. Horowitz M: Stress response syndromes, character style and dynamic psychotherapy. Arch Gen Psychiatry 31:768-781, 1974

34. Lindy JD, Grace MC, Breen BL, et al: Psychotherapy with survivors of the Beverly Hills Supper Club fire. Am J Psychotherapy 37:593-610, 1983

35. U.S. Bureau of the Census: Statistical Abstract of the United States Bureau of the Census. Washington, DC, U.S. Government Printing Office, 1985

36. Check WA: Homicide, suicide and other violence gain increasing medical attention. JAMA 245:721-730, 1985

37. Lundin T: Morbidity following sudden and unexpected bereavement. Br J Psychiatry 144:84-88, 1984

Chapter 6

The Prediction of Outcome in Bereavement

Stephen B. Shanfield, M.D.

Chapter 6

The Prediction of Outcome in Bereavement

During bereavement, many survivors experience increased psychiatric morbidity, increased illness behavior, a diminished sense of well-being, and even increased mortality (1–9). These problems occur with considerable frequency and have implications for public policy, since many of the bereaved who experience poor outcomes use a disproportionate share of health care resources (9). While the outcome process has been relatively well described, particularly in spouse survivors, factors that predict poor outcome have been less well researched. This chapter will describe variables that portend problems during the bereavement period for adult survivors, which can often be assessed prior to the death of the loved one (10). In addition, variables that suggest the possibility of a good outcome will be described.

There are many current and excellent reviews of bereavement outcome (1–7, 9). Most studies of adult bereavement are of the widowed, although there is small and recent literature on adult child loss (1, 5, 11–13). The bulk of observations have been made during the bereavement period after the death of the loved one. For greater detail about outcome, the reader is referred to the reviews, since the description of outcome presented here will be brief.

Factors that portend vulnerability to poor outcome have also been reviewed in the same literature. These factors have been researched less systematically and usually the studies have been of widows (14), although recently risk factors have been described in other bereaved populations (11–13). In this literature, little effort has been made to link vulnerability factors to specific outcomes. The following will discuss risk factors as they are associated with a particular bereavement outcome. Vulnerability factors are summarized in Table 1.

PSYCHIATRIC DISTRESS

Many authors note the presence of depression, anxiety, fear of decompensation, appetite changes, insomnia, and nightmares following the loss of a spouse (6, 15). Indeed, Clayton reports that 45 percent of widows become clinically depressed during the first year of bereavement and that 17 percent remain depressed at 13 months (16). Similarly, although in a different bereaved population, Shanfield and colleagues note that parents who lose adult children as a result of accidents have higher than expected levels of psychiatric symptoms, including depression (12, 13).

A number of factors are implicated in the etiology of increased psychiatric distress in the form of psychiatric symptoms during the bereavement period.

Table 1. Summary of Poor Outcome Vulnerability Factors

Psychiatric Disturbance, Including Depression

1. Prebereavement psychiatric disturbance, including depression
2. Manner of death of deceased
   a. Illness longer than six months in spouse
   b. Sudden death
3. Family life cycle variables
   a. Younger age of survivor at death
      Widow under age 45
   b. Younger age of deceased at death
      Death of young adult child—particularly for mothers
4. Dysfunctional marital and family relationships
5. Constriction of capacity to express feelings
6. Compromised financial status

Increased Illness Behavior

1. Prebereavement chronic illness
2. Tendency to somaticize under stress
3. Mother of deceased young adult child
4. Constriction of capacity to express feelings
5. Manner of death of deceased—sudden death
6. Prebereavement cognitive impairment

Diminished Quality of Life

1. Prebereavement psychiatric disturbance, including depression
2. Manner of death of deceased
   a. Illness longer than six months for widow
   b. Sudden death of adult child
3. Dysfunctional marital and family relationships
4. Few perceived social supports
5. Compromised financial status

Increased Mortality

1. Prebereavement chronic illness
2. Prebereavement cognitive impairment

Premorbid Psychiatric Difficulties

Premorbid psychiatric difficulties have been best studied in widows and in individuals who have emotional difficulties, particularly depression, before the death of their loved ones. This population appears to be at risk for continuance and even worsening of psychiatric symptoms during the bereavement period (6, 17). The emotional resiliency needed to adequately adjust to the changes wrought by a chronic illness and the death of a spouse is impaired by a psychiatric symptomatic state. Coping with the changes brought on by a chronic illness preceding the death of a spouse, as well as coping with the inevitable psychosocial changes that occur during the bereavement period, is particularly difficult for depressed individuals.

Manner of Death

The manner in which a person dies has been cited as a factor underlying psychiatric problems in the bereaved. For instance, a widow who survives the death of a mate after an illness lasting longer than six months seems to be at greater risk for depression during the bereavement period (18). Presumably, in this instance, the spouse becomes psychologically depleted while caring for the ill mate. At the other end of the time spectrum, sudden and unexpected death has also been noted to portend increased emotional difficulties for the widowed survivor (6, 9). This is also true for parents who lose adult children suddenly (for example, in traffic accidents) (12). These parents have higher levels of psychiatric symptoms than parents whose adult children die slowly of cancer (13).

Family Life Cycle Variables

A family life cycle perspective is important in understanding the outcome of bereavement (13). This perspective holds that the nature of family relationships is different at different times of the life cycle and that these relationships are important mediators of the response to the loss. Thus, widows under the age of 45 appear to be at risk for a poor emotional outcome, including depression (6, 16). Presumably, these women have experienced a large number of intense losses as a result of the death of their husbands. These losses include not only the loss of a husband, provider, and father for their children, but a truncated future and the loss of an ongoing source of emotional and financial support (6).

Similarly, parents who lose young adult children have higher levels of psychiatric symptoms than parents who lose older children (13). In this instance, each parent group is at a different point in its family development at the time of their children's deaths. Parents of young adult children have not separated as much from their children as have parents of older children. The young adult children are still an important part of their parents' lives, and this is an important determinant of outcome in this group (13). Moreover, mothers who lose young adult children in traffic accidents are more likely to have a bereavement characterized by higher psychiatric distress, including depression, than fathers. This points to a different pattern of grief among women and suggests a different pattern of relationship between mothers and their young adult children (12).

Dysfunctional Relationship with Deceased

A dysfunctional relationship with the deceased has been described by various authors as having a potential for increased emotional difficulties, including depression, during the bereavement period (7, 19, 20). A family systems model provides a helpful perspective for understanding the genesis of psychiatric problems in these bereaved individuals. Marital system variables, such as domination of one spouse over the other, authoritarianism, skewed decision-making, lack of resolution of conflict, and insensitivity to feelings often portend problems for the survivors in the bereavement period (14). For bereaved individuals who are dependent and subservient, and who had a symbiotic attachment to the deceased, the loss is considerably greater than in relationships characterized by autonomy and negotiation of conflict (6, 20). These individuals have to put more energy into learning about functioning on their own during the recovery period. Similarly, the widowed who were authoritarian in their marriage have lost a great deal since they now have no one to do their bidding. In these instances, the loss of a spouse can result in increased levels of psychiatric distress. A relationship characterized by preexisting marital difficulties, particularly of marked ambivalence or hate, is also thought to bode poorly for psychiatric adjustment during the bereavement period (15, 19). Ambivalent elements directed at the spouse are also an internalized part of the self and remain with the survivor. Indeed, the loss of the hated object must be dealt with during the bereavement period, and this can result in increased distress. These variables are similar to those that have been described in dysfunctional families who have diminished interactional competence (21, 22).

Marital interaction can also become dysfunctional as a result of chronic illness. For instance, there are many reports of overprotectiveness of wives toward husbands who have had a myocardial infarction (23). In the event of death, these surviving spouses can also face increased psychological difficulties during the bereavement period.

Constricted Capacity to Express Emotion

Studying widows after the death of a spouse, Maddison and Viola note that individuals who suppress emotion are at high risk for problems during the bereavement period (15). Similarly, Parkes notes that individuals whose family system discourages the expression of grief are judged to be at risk during the bereavement period (10). Constriction of affect can often be an integral part of the marital interaction and makes it difficult to tolerate the inevitable intensity of feelings associated with the response to loss. This too can result in increased psychiatric symptoms during the bereavement period (6, 21, 22, 24, 25).

Compromised Financial Status

Bereaved individuals whose financial resources are seriously compromised as a result of an illness and subsequent death of a loved one face a difficult social adjustment. This also leads to considerable psychiatric distress (6).

INCREASED ILLNESS BEHAVIOR

Many bereaved individuals have an increase in illness behavior. For instance, as many as 40 percent of surviving widows consult doctors for headaches, dizziness, and other psychophysiologic symptoms during the bereavement period (17, 26). There is a 25 percent deterioration in health during the first 13 months following the loss of a spouse, and this may be especially true of widows (9, 15). Indeed, there may be as much as a threefold increase in hospitalization rates during the first year of widowhood (26). Parkes notes that psychiatric hospitalizations increase approximately sixfold during the bereavement period (6). Widows, particularly under age 65, tend to undergo an increased and sustained intake of hypnotic medication, alcohol, and tranquilizers (6, 17).

Jacobs and Ostfeld note that one likely explanation for increased medical problems during the bereavement period is that widows are not able to maintain their health status in the absence of a helpful spouse (4). With the loss of a mate, they may not have someone to provide encouragement for and support of adaptive behaviors. If acutely or chronically ill, they no longer have a mate to help them with nutrition, to take medications, and to visit doctors. This, coupled with a relative lack of the necessary skills to care for themselves, can result in a decline in health status.

Often, somatic complaints accompany psychiatric symptoms. This may be a partial explanation for the observation that parents of young adult children who have died in traffic accidents have more health complaints during the bereavement period compared to before the death, and compared to an older group of parents whose children have died of cancer. These parents of accident victims also have a greater number of psychiatric symptoms than expected (12, 13). In this instance, the health complaints and psychiatric symptoms are part of the general coloration of the grief response among parents of children who have died in traffic accidents. Most likely, both the relative youth and the sudden, unexpected nature of the death contribute to the parents' distress after such tragic, fatal accidents.

Individuals who tend to somaticize when under psychologic stress may also have increased somatic complaints during the bereavement period. These can also account for increased illness behavior.

Difficulty in the ability to express feelings is also associated with a tendency to somaticize (24) and this has been noted in the bereaved (25). The expression of grief in this group may be in nonpsychological terms, particularly in terms of bodily injury where inner psychic distress is often communicated by means of physical complaints (24, 25).

Spouse survivors who are cognitively impaired and who were cared for by their deceased spouses face particularly difficult times during the bereavement period. These individuals, if seriously disabled, may require placement in a long-term care setting. They also run the risk of developing intercurrent illness and even death, as has been noted in cognitively impaired populations (27).

DIMINISHED QUALITY OF LIFE

For many bereaved survivors, the subjective sense of well-being diminishes. This dimension of the quality of an individual's life is distinct and largely independent (28), although correlated with levels of health and physical disability, socioeconomic status, marital status, and depression (28). Quality of life can be measured in many ways, from global assessments (29) to assessments of the level of morale, to levels of maturation as a result of the changes wrought by the loss.

Diminished well-being is noted in individuals who were distressed during the prebereavement period (6). Widows who survive their husbands after an illness of longer than six months are more likely to become psychologically depleted and have a lower sense of the quality of their lives. A family life cycle perspective is also helpful in understanding a diminished sense of well-being. For instance, as already mentioned, the sudden death of an adult child in a traffic accident produces more distress for parents than the death of an adult child from cancer.

A dysfunctional family relationship, notably ambivalence in the marital relationship, can be a forerunner of increased suffering and guilt during the bereavement period and can result in a decreased sense of well-being (6). Similarly, a symbiotic attachment to the deceased portends increased suffering and a lowering of the quality of life for the bereaved survivor (6, 8, 19).

Grief is often reactivated at anniversaries and with other affectively laden experiences that evoke memories and images of the deceased. This can be intensely distressing and can transiently lower the quality of life (30, 31).

A diminished sense of well-being is seen in many survivors who feel lonely and at the same time cut off from finding other relationships (7, 32). Indeed, the perception of few social supports is associated with increased distress during the bereavement period (6, 7). Some may be too depressed to utilize an already existing support network. In addition, a recent move to a new area before the death of their loved one can preclude the establishment of a social network. While family and friends are the normal sources of support in the crises of illness and death, sustained support is not possible if they are at a distance. In this instance, the survivor is at risk for more of a decline in the quality of life than those who are more firmly established socially.

Many bereaved individuals experience a drop in income and can become financially compromised as a result of a loss (6). This can create considerable distress about the quality of survival and can diminish the sense of well-being. Psychological energy utilized in adjusting to the inevitable changes of bereavement is diverted to adjusting to the financial realities of survival. Furthermore, options that discretionary money can provide the bereaved, such as trips to visit family and participating in recreational activities, become impossible, and this can perpetuate a diminished quality of life.

INCREASED MORTALITY RATE

A number of investigators note that the widowed have an increased rate of mortality during the bereavement period (33, 5, 34). In these studies, there is as great as a sevenfold increase in mortality rate over baseline expectancies during the first year following loss. At least for women, these rates may increase in the second and third year (33, 34). Widowed men aged 55–74 appear to have a higher mortality rate (35).

The lack of health care maintenance has also been implicated as an explanation for the increase in mortality in spouse survivors (36). The bereaved may take less responsibility for the management of their health. They may neglect early signs of disease, or fail to manage chronic disease because of the influence of despair or grief. Similarly, the presence of cognitive impairment, either dementia or delirium, is a serious concern in the bereaved and portends the possibility of increased mortality (27).

PREDICTORS OF GOOD OUTCOME

A number of variables are noted clinically to be associated with good bereavement outcome, which is characterized by a relative increase in the sense of personal growth as a result of the death of a loved one and an increased quality of life. These factors are summarized in Table 2.

An optimistic view of the world associated with a belief system that allows the bereaved to transcend the loss is helpful in dealing with the death of a loved one. Good health allows the bereavement process to proceed normally, without the added intrusion of having to deal with the psychosocial and medical consequences of ill health. Similarly, having adequate financial resources allows for increased options in dealing with the loss, including obtaining psychiatric therapy. While the pain of grief is not eradicated, expanded options can make life somewhat easier during the bereavement period. Similarly, having a solid support group provides a basis for easing the emotional and social burden of bereavement. Work can provide a source of meaningful structure which can sustain one through the difficult time of bereavement. In a similar manner, a sense of self-sufficiency is a helpful trait in adjusting to the changes wrought by the death.

Table 2. Summary of Good Outcome Predictor Variables

Summary of Good Outcome Predictor Variables
Good Health
Prebereavement good health
Quality of Life
Sense of optimism
Transcendent belief system
Self-sufficient
Experience with loss
Competent family interaction
Solid social network
Adequate financial resources

Experience with loss appears to foster maturation in that individuals who have previously dealt with the stress of bereavement tend to have fewer psychiatric symptoms. It appears that learning about one's response to loss protects one later in other bereavement experiences (12).

DISCUSSION

A number of vulnerability factors are specifically linked to the bereavement outcomes of psychiatric distress, increased illness behavior, diminished quality of life, and increased mortality. For instance, prebereavement difficulties portend problems for the bereaved survivor. Those with psychiatric distress or chronic illness usually continue with these problems, which may even worsen during the bereavement period. Well-being is frequently diminished in these individuals. A chronically ill survivor also runs the risk of increased mortality. Cognitive impairment portends the possibility of serious outcome difficulties during bereavement and can result in increased utilization of health care resources, and can even result in death.

The manner of death is also a determinant of bereavement outcome. For instance, sudden death is associated with increased psychiatric distress and illness behavior as well as diminished well-being among bereaved survivors. An illness lasting longer than six months in spouses is similarly related to increased levels of psychiatric symptoms and a lowered sense of well-being among widows. Furthermore, family life cycle variables are determinants of increased psychiatric disturbance in survivors. For instance, widows under the age of 45 and parents who have lost young adult children are often more symptomatic during the bereavement period. Often, a dysfunctional relationship with the deceased is a forerunner of increased distress and a diminished quality of life among survivors. Likewise, the constriction of the capacity to express feelings is associated with increased psychiatric distress and illness behavior among the bereaved. Increased illness behavior may also be seen in survivors who somaticize when under stress. Among the bereaved who are financially compromised as a result of the death of a loved one, increased psychiatric distress and diminished well-being can be seen. Moreover, bereaved survivors with few social supports can also have a decreased quality of life.

The prediction of poor bereavement outcome has implications for the prevention of psychiatric and medical morbidity. Knowledge of risk factors provides a key to targeting those who can benefit from early intervention. Many of these factors can be assessed in the about-to-be-bereaved. The reduction of morbidity carries with it the promise of a decrease in the use of health care resources and the expenditure of health care dollars. This is, however, early in our understanding of risk factors as they relate to outcome. There is a need for systematic research in vulnerability to a poor bereavement outcome.

Factors that portend vulnerability to a poor bereavement outcome are nonspecific. These factors also predict outcome to other major change events, such as major medical illness. In this sense, bereavement is only one model of psychosocial change. Thus, vulnerable individuals, after a myocardial infarction or after the onset of cancer, face a difficult adjustment during their convalescence. For instance, individuals who have a heart attack and who are premorbidly depressed often have increased psychiatric problems during the postinfarct period.

Finally, indicators of good bereavement outcome provide an understanding of optimal psychosocial functioning, particularly in the context of the stress of severe illness and death. They are even less well researched than poor outcome indicators but provide insight into good health and well-being. They, too, merit further investigation.

REFERENCES

1. Bowlby J: Attachment and Loss, volume III: Loss. New York, Basic Books, 1980
2. Clayton PJ: The clinical morbidity of the first year of bereavement: a review. Compr Psychiatry 14:151-157, 1973
3. Epstein G, Weitz L, Roback H, et al: Research and bereavement: a selective and critical review. Compr Psychiatry 16:537-546, 1975
4. Jacobs S, Ostfeld A: An epidemiological review of the mortality of bereavement. Psychosom Med 39:344-357, 1977
5. Osterweis M, Solomon F, Green M: Bereavement: Reactions, Consequences and Care. Washington, DC, National Academy Press, 1984
6. Parkes CM: Bereavement: Studies of Grief in Adult Life. New York, International Universities Press, 1972
7. Raphael B: The Anatomy of Bereavement. New York, Basic Books, 1983
8. Shanfield SB: Social and emotional determinants of the death process. Ariz Med 36:602-603, 1979
9. Shanfield SB: Illness and bereavement: unrecognized implications for prevention. Ariz Med 23:444-446, 1981
10. Parkes CM: Psychological aspects, in The Management of Terminal Disease. Edited by Saunders C. London, Edward Arnold, 1979
11. Shanfield SB, Benjamin GAH, Swain BJ: Parents' reaction to the death of an adult child from cancer. Am J Psychiatry 141:1092-1094, 1984
12. Shanfield SB, Swain BJ: Death of adult children in traffic accidents. J Nerv Ment Dis 1172:533-538, 1984
13. Shanfield SB, Swain BJ, Benjamin GAH: Parents' responses to the death of adult children from accidents and cancer: a comparison. Omega (in press)
14. Shanfield SB: Predicting bereavement outcome: marital factors. Family Systems Medicine 1:40-46, 1983
15. Maddison D, Viola A: The health of widows in the year following bereavement. J Psychosom Res 12:297-306, 1968
16. Clayton PJ: The sequelae and nonsequelae of conjugal bereavement. Am J Psychiatry 136:1530-1534, 1979
17. Clayton PJ: Mortality and morbidity in the first year of widowhood. Arch Gen Psychiatry 30:747-750, 1974
18. Gerber I, Rusalem R, Hannon N, et al: Anticipatory grief and aged widows and widowers. J Gerontol 30:225-229, 1975

19. Freud S: Mourning and melancholia (1917), in Complete Psychological Works, Standard Edition, vol 14. Translated and edited by Strachey J. London, Hogarth Press, 1961

20. Hirschfeld RMA, Klerman GL, Gough HC, et al: A measure of interpersonal dependency. J Pers Assess 4:611-618, 1977

21. Beavers WR, Hampson RB, Hulgus YF: Commentary: the Beavers system approach to family assessment. Fam Process 24:398-405, 1985

22. Lewis JM, Beavers WR, Gossett JT, et al: No Single Thread: Psychological Health in Family Systems. New York, Brunner/Mazel, 1976

23. Doehrman SR: Psychosocial aspects of recovery from coronary heart disease: a review. Soc Sci Med 11:199-218, 1977

24. Taylor GJ: Alexithymia: concept, measurement, and implications for treatment. Am J Psychiatry 141:725-732, 1984

25. Warnes H: Alexithymia and the grieving process. Psychiatr J Univ Ottawa 10:41-44, 1985

26. Glick IO, Weiss RS, Parkes CM: The First Year of Bereavement. New York, John Wiley & Sons, 1974

27. Lipowski ZJ: Transient cognitive disorders (delirium, acute confusional states) in the elderly. Am J Psychiatry 140:1426-1436, 1983

28. Larson R: Thirty years of research on the subjective well-being of older Americans. J Gerontol 35:109-125, 1978

29. Lehman AF: The effects of psychiatric symptoms on quality of life assessments among the chronically mentally ill. Evaluation and Program Planning 6:143-151, 1983

30. Horowitz MJ: Stress Response Syndromes. New York, Jason Aronson, 1976

31. Pollock GH: Anniversary reactions, trauma, and mourning. Psychoanal Q 39:347-371, 1970

32. Parkes CM, Weiss RS: Recovery from Bereavement. New York, Basic Books, 1983

33. Cox PR, Ford JR: The mortality of widows shortly after widowhood. Lancet 1:163-164, 1967

34. Rees DW, Lutkins SG: Mortality of bereavement. Br Med J 4:13-16, 1967

35. Helsing KJ, Szklo M: Mortality after bereavement. Am J Epidemiol 114:41-52, 1981

36. Jacobs S, Douglas L: Grief: a mediating process between a loss and illness. Compr Psychiatry 20:165-176, 1979

Chapter 7

The Texas Revised Inventory of Grief

Thomas R. Faschingbauer, Ph.D.
Sidney Zisook, M.D.
Richard DeVaul, M.D.

Chapter 7

The Texas Revised Inventory of Grief

Grieving the loss of a loved one is a common human experience with profound medical and mental health repercussions. Yet we are not aware of any simple paper-and-pencil test for measuring grief. Most published studies of grief have consisted mainly of microcosmic anecdotes about individual grief reactions or macrocosmic statistical analyses of large numbers of bereaved persons without much effort to quantify specific grief reactions (see Chapter 8). The construct of grief has not yet been fully operationalized or validated. This chapter reports on the development of the brief paper-and-pencil questionnaire, Texas Revised Inventory of Grief (TRIG), which is meant to help quantify and measure the intensity of grief reactions.

The TRIG is a two-scale Likert-type measure of grief following bereavement. It was developed using factor analysis, is easily administered and scored, and permits rapid evaluation of the extremity and nature of an individual's personal reaction to bereavement. The extremity of grief reactions can be compared to average reactions for approximately 100 "normative" individuals at each of four time intervals after bereavement. The nature of a person's reaction can be determined by comparing his or her scores to standard scores on the two scales. Complicated grief reactions are often immediately obvious.

The TRIG contains a set of clinical, demographic, and psychographic questions (for example, "How close were you to the person who died?"), as well as space to communicate in an open-ended or unstructured way any additional feelings, circumstances, and problems surrounding bereavement. Items comprising the TRIG appear to measure grief as a present emotion of longing, as an adjustment to a past life event with several stages, as a medical/psychological outcome, and as a personal experience. Furthermore, this assessment is rapidly done with a minimum of intrusion into the bereaved person's already disrupted life.

DEVELOPMENT OF THE TEXAS REVISED INVENTORY OF GRIEF

In keeping with the notion that self-report measures are at least as accurate as either behavioral or physiological observations in the measurement of emotion, Faschingbauer and colleagues administered a 14-item self-rated questionnaire to 57 psychiatric outpatients who had lost a loved one to death (1). Internal consistency analyses revealed two sets of items that correlated more highly with their total scores than they did with each other. One set of seven items, referring to present feelings, had a median correlation of +.69 with total score, a split half reliability correlation of +.81, and significantly differentiated between subjects with recent and not so recent (over two years) object losses. The other set of four items, referring to behavior immediately following the object loss, showed a median internal consistency of +.70.

An expanded version of this questionnaire (58 items) was sent to friends and colleagues around the country. Each was asked to have one or two of their friends or neighbors who had lost a loved one to death complete the questionnaire. Completed questionnaires (*N* = 260) were received from all areas of the United States. Table 1

Table 1. Demographic Data on Two Subsamples of the Present Research Sample

Demographic Variable	Percentage of U.S. Initial Sample (*N* = 260)	Percentage of Houston Replication Sample (*N* = 328)	Percentage of U.S. 1975 Census
Mean Age in Years	38	33	28
Sex, Male	37	28	49
Race			
Caucasian	64	69	87
Black	30	3	12
Other	6	27	1
Annual Income			
$ 0– 9,999	32	7	36
$10,000–24,999	42	44	53
$25,000 and up	27	49	12
Religion			
Jewish	5	10	5
Protestant	40	58	55
Roman Catholic	26	22	38
Other or none	29	10	2

compares our initial U.S. sample, as well as 328 subjects from a later replication sample, to 1975 U.S. census figures and shows that the experimental sample contained more older persons, females, blacks, and members of upper income families than did the census. In part, this may reflect the fact that the census figures were at least two years old and were not limited to the bereaved. However, other differences (such as income) likely reflect our choices of friends and our friends' choices of friends and neighbors.

Each item was scored one to five, with five representing the greatest degree of grief at the time of response. All values for the items were defined based on clinical experience and the existing literature. Factor analysis was performed by the SPSS Factor program for a principal factoring analysis (PA2) with varimax rotation (2).

Fourteen relatively distinct factors were derived from the factor analysis of the items, and only those factors with eigenvalues greater than 1.00 for rotation initially were retained (3). Those items loading .40 or higher on any of the first three factors, without any loading on any other factor higher than .75 times their primary factor loading, were selected for inclusion in an iterative internal consistency analysis. Only the first two factors had sufficient numbers of these "non-overlapping" items to constitute useful scales. Table 2 shows the wordings of the final items, the changes in their correlations with total scale scores as the lower correlating items were deleted, and the final intercorrelations among the items themselves. A more detailed explanation of, and rationale for, the statistical methods utilized can be found in the TRIG's Scoring Manual (4).

DESCRIPTION OF THE TEXAS REVISED INVENTORY OF GRIEF

Demographic/Psychographic Data

The TRIG answer sheet begins with demographic information about the bereaved person (name, age, sex, race, education, and religion) (see Table 3). Next is a series of questions about the deceased person's age, duration since they died, their relationship to the bereaved, how close that relationship was, and how suddenly and unexpectedly they died.

Part I: Past Behavior

The respondent is asked to "think back to the time this person died" in answering the eight items in Part I. These items were psychometrically "distilled" from 13 nonoverlapping items with an initial median correlation with their total score of .65. After reducing the

Table 2. TRIG Scale Statistics

Item content	Inter-item vs. Items with Internal Consistency r^s			Scale Total Minus Item Median Inter-item r^s		Reliability: Split	Half	Coeff.	Alpha
	Development Orig.	Development Final	Replication	Development	Replication	Development	Replication	Development	Replication
Scale One (Part II): Present Emotion of Grief									
1. I still cry . . .	71	72	72	53	46				
2. I still get upset	77	78	72	53	44				
3. I cannot accept	71	69	63	57	42				
4. Sometimes . . . miss . . .	69	70	47*	54	32				
5. . . . Painful to recall	68	69	60	52	40				
6. I am preoccupied . . .	73	74	71	54	44	88	82	86	89
7. I hide my tears . . .	67	64	63	50	37				
8. No one . . . take place . . .	63	63	44*	45	29				
9. Can't avoid thinking	69	69	59	52	39				
10. Feel it's unfair . . .	63	63	57	46	38				
11. Things still remind . . .	66	66	54	50	35				
12. Unable to accept . . .	65	65	59	46	40				
13. Still . . . need to cry.	71	71	65	51	42				
Scale Two (Part I): Past Life Disruption									
1. Hard to get along . . .	63	66	68	47	49				
2. . . . Hard to work . . .	68	70	68	53	51				
3. . . . Lost interest . . .	67	68	65	41	49				
4. Do what deceased did	56	53	57	40	42	74	79	77	87
5. Unusually irritable	66	67	67	48	50				
6. Couldn't keep up	68	68	74	47	54				
7. Angry . . . left me	51	52	48	38	36				
8. Hard to sleep	64	61	68	47	56				

Note: Development $N = 260$; Replication $N = 145$

*Though these values are low and suggest item instability, the ratios to interitem median r^s are higher than original ratios.

item pool to the highest eight, this correlation rose to .67. These final eight items overlap about 40 percent with their total score and only about 22 percent with each other. Their alpha coefficient, which approximates the lower level of test-retest reliability (5) was .77, and their split half reliability was .74. In content, these items sample a variety of life events that might be disrupted by grief (see Table 2). The objective nature of these events is reflected in the plot of means, which declines only slightly over time (see Figure 1).

We attempted to assess construct validity for Part I by hypothesizing that the deaths of persons active and important in the daily life affairs of the bereaved would produce greater levels of life disruption than those less actively involved. A subhypothesis was that females, who in our culture traditionally have been rewarded for dependency on others and who often are financially dependent on their husbands' incomes, would suffer greater life disruption following a death than males, whose life training and culturally stereotyped role behavior usually encourages self-sufficiency (6). Student's t statistic indicated that this was the case, as females demonstrated significantly higher scores on Part I than males ($p < .05$).

A second subhypothesis was that the death of a working-age adult

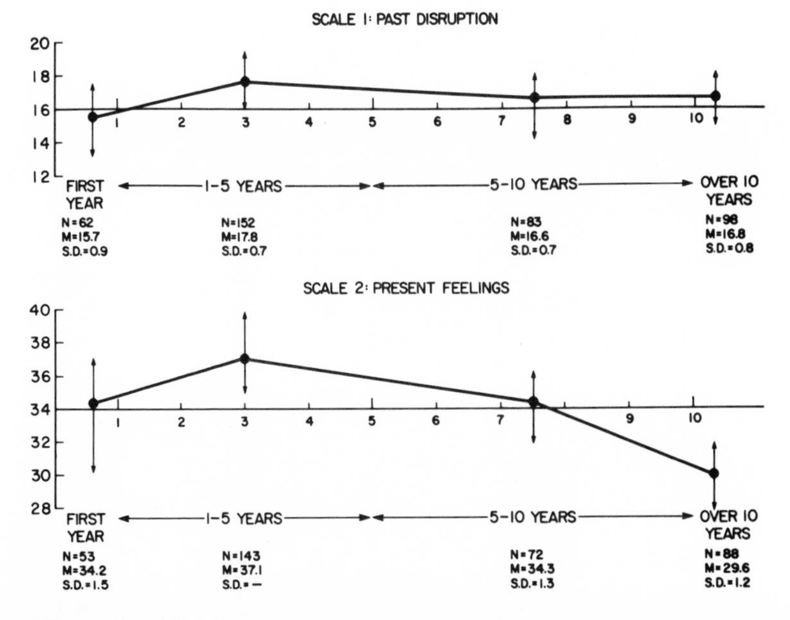

Figure 1. TRIG norms and 95 percent confidence intervals.

Table 3. The Texas Revised Inventory of Grief*

Name or #:__________ Age:____ Sex:____ Race: ☐ White ☐ Black ☐ Lat. Am. ☐ Oriental ☐ Other (list)
Circle Last Year of Formal Schooling Completed:
1 2 3 4 5 6 7 8 9 10 11 12 13 14 15 16 17 or more.
Religion: ☐ Protestant ☐ Catholic ☐ Jewish ☐ Other (list)
The person who died was my (check only one): Father ☐ Mother ☐ Brother ☐ Sister ☐ Husband ☐
Wife ☐ Son ☐ Daughter ☐ Friend ☐ Other (list) ☐

LOOKING BACK, I WOULD GUESS THAT MY RELATIONSHIP WITH THIS PERSON WAS (check only one):
☐ Closer than any relationship I've ever had before or since.
☐ Closer than most relationships I've had with other people.
☐ About as close as most of my relationships with others.
☐ Not as close as most of my relationships.
☐ Not very close at all.

PLEASE COMPLETE A SEPARATE FORM FOR EACH PERSON WHO DIED.

HOW OLD WAS THIS PERSON WHEN THEY DIED?________.

THIS PERSON DIED (check only one box):

☐ within the past 3 months	☐ 9–12 months ago	☐ 5–10 years ago
☐ 3–6 months ago	☐ 1–2 years ago	☐ 10–20 years ago
☐ 6–9 months ago	☐ 2–5 years ago	☐ more than 20 years ago

THIS PERSON'S DEATH WAS: ☐ Expected ☐ Unexpected ☐ Slow ☐ Sudden

PART I: PAST BEHAVIOR

Think back to the time this person died and answer all of these items about your feelings and actions at that time by indicating whether each item is Completely True, Mostly True, Both True and False, Mostly False, or Completely False as it applied to you after this person died. Check the best answer.

	COMPL. TRUE	MOSTLY TRUE	TRUE & FALSE	MOSTLY FALSE	COMPL. FALSE
1. After this person died I found it hard to get along with certain people..........					
2. I found it hard to work well after this person died					
3. After this person's death I lost interest in my family, friends, and outside activities					
4. I felt a need to do things that the deceased had wanted to do					
5. I was unusually irritable after this person died					
6. I couldn't keep up with my normal activities for the first 3 months after this person died................................					
7. I was angry that the person who died left me...					
8. I found it hard to sleep after this person died					

PART II: PRESENT FEELINGS

Now answer all of the following items by checking how you presently feel about this person's death. Do not look back at Part I.

	COMPL. TRUE	MOSTLY TRUE	TRUE & FALSE	MOSTLY FALSE	COMPL. FALSE
1. I still cry when I think of the person who died					
2. I still get upset when I think about the person who died					
3. I cannot accept this person's death					
4. Sometimes I very much miss the person who died					
5. Even now it's painful to recall memories of the person who died					
6. I am preoccupied with thoughts (often think) about the person who died					
7. I hide my tears when I think about the person who died					
8. No one will ever take the place in my life of the person who died					
9. I can't avoid thinking about the person who died					
10. I feel it's unfair that this person died					
11. Things and people around me still remind me of the person who died					
12. I am unable to accept the death of the person who died					
13. At times I still feel the need to cry for the person who died					

PART III: RELATED FACTS

Now please answer the following items by circling either True or False.

1. I attended the funeral of the person who died.	True	False
2. I feel that I have really grieved for the person who died.	True	False
3. I feel that I am now functioning about as well as I was before the death.	True	False
4. I seem to get upset each year at about the same time as the person died.	True	False
5. Sometimes I feel that I have the same illness as the person who died.	True	False

THANK YOU FOR ANSWERING ALL OF THESE QUESTIONS. WE ARE ALSO VERY INTERESTED IN YOUR SPECIAL THOUGHTS AND COMMENTS. PLEASE USE THE REST OF THIS SIDE TO TELL US ABOUT ANY THOUGHTS AND FEELINGS YOU HAVE.

____

____

____

____

____

____

would produce a greater life disruption than that of an older adult, who may have been less likely to be actively involved in the day-to-day "business" of the family, and whose death might be considered more "natural." Using Student's *t* statistic, this hypothesis was supported. Part I scores were significantly ($p < .02$) higher for those bereaved subjects where the deceased was a younger (< 30) adult than for those where an older family member had died (> 75).

Additional studies, including the Houston Replication Sample (see Table 1), looked at the relationship of Part I scores to funeral attendance. We hypothesized that those bereaved individuals who attended the funerals of their deceased loved ones would have a better adjustment to their deaths. This hypothesis derives from psychomedical "folklore" that attendance at the funeral of the deceased bodes well for subsequent adjustment. It also seems to touch on the somewhat paradoxical finding of humanistically oriented theorists that "nadir" experiences like grief may promote personal growth and adjustment. Here it was assumed that funeral attendance provides a religious or philosophical basis for integrating the loss in a meaningful way with other life experiences. Because of the philosophical, religious, and other social supports that a funeral provides the bereaved, it was hypothesized that those 23 subjects who reportedly had not attended the deceased person's funeral would score significantly higher on Part I than the 305 persons who reported they did attend the entire funeral. Analysis of covariance, controlling for the sex of the bereaved and his or her relationship to the deceased, showed just such a difference, with funeral attenders scoring lower on Part I than nonattenders ($p < .05$).

Part I, therefore, does seem to be a reasonably reliable and valid measure of one's initial adjustment to the death of a loved one.

Part II: Present Feelings

Part II was psychometrically "distilled" from 26 nonoverlapping items. Its median internal consistency was .61 initially, which rose to .69 after eliminating 13 of those items with lower correlations with total score. The 13 final items overlap about 47 percent with their total score and about 26 percent with each other, suggesting that they are measuring grief from several different angles.

This low level of inter-item overlap seems, at first, inconsistent with the wording of these items, many of which appear to rephrase item 4 ("Sometimes I very much miss the person who died"). Closer inspection of the items, however, reveals that thoughts, feelings, memories, opinions, and attitudes are all being tapped by Part II. That the subjects were not answering these items alike on the basis of their conceptual similarity (7) was suggested by the means and standard deviations for various intervals after bereavement. The trend of these means (see Figure 1) suggests that whatever emotion is measured by Part II worsens after the first year, but then declines steadily over time, as one would expect the emotion of grief to do (8, 9). Coefficient alpha was .86 for Part II and the split half reliability was .88 (see Table 2).

Construct validity of Part II was assessed by testing two distinct hypotheses. First, it was hypothesized that bereaved females would score higher on Part II than would males, since emotional awareness and expression has traditionally been suppressed among Western males ("Big boys don't cry") (6). Student's t statistic showed this to be the case for our initial sample ($p < .05$). Second, it was hypothesized that because of their greater cultural closeness, spouses would likely experience greater levels of grief emotion than would other nonblood relatives. Part II scores were indeed significantly higher for the bereaved spouses ($p < .05$).

Part II, then, does seem to reliably and validly measure present levels of grief, an emotion whose intensity varies as a function of time, sex, and degree of relatedness to the bereaved.

Combining Parts I and II

In addition to measuring both past adjustments and present feelings, the TRIG appears to provide information regarding a person's progress through the various stages of grief by combining Parts I and II. It was hoped that two orthogonal measures of grief might function much as do measures of barometric pressure and temperature in delineating seasonal weather changes. Table 4 shows the hypothesized relationship between Parts I and II and various types of grief adjustment patterns. High and low scorers were above and below the 50th percentile, respectively, on each part.

The construct validity of this bivariate approach to grief adjustment was assessed by testing two hypotheses: 1) that the groups in Table

Table 4. Grief Reaction Groups

Part I Past	Part II Present	Group Name
Low	Low	Group 1: Absence of grief
Low	High	Group 2: Delayed grief
High	High	Group 3: Prolonged grief
High	Low	Group 4: Acute resolved grief

4 would vary as a function of social support right after the death, and 2) that they would vary in subsequent health patterns. It was hoped that indirect support for both the humanistic-personal growth and medical-psychological theories might be obtained in this way.

The first hypothesis was assessed by calculating the percentage of persons in each group who had attended the funeral of the deceased. Whereas 100 percent of the 74 persons in grief Group 1 (low on both parts) had attended the funeral, only 93 and 92 percent, respectively, of groups 2 and 3 (where present grief feelings were high) had attended the funeral, as had only 88 percent of Group 4. Chi square analysis showed that this distribution was significantly different from chance ($\chi^2 = 8.45, p < .04$), suggesting that the present fourfold typology is meaningful in terms of personal adjustment.

The second hypothesis, that the four groups would vary in health patterns, was assessed by using a shortened version of the Severity of Illness Rating Scale (10). We asked 355 bereaved persons to indicate which illnesses they had experienced and for which of the illnesses they had sought medical aid in the past two years. Each illness had been rated by over 300 physicians as to its severity. Total scores across illnesses were assessed using analysis of covariance. We hypothesized that since we had sampled only persons who had suffered the death of a loved one, low scores on both scales (Group 1) could be taken to imply an absence of conscious grief with subsequent moderate somatic manifestations. Less illness was expected among those persons (Group 4) who had high scores on Part I (past disruption) and low scores on Part II (present grief level), since they had apparently grieved and had resolved their grief. Greater illness was expected among subjects (Groups 2 and 3) with high Part II scores regardless of their Part I scores, since unresolved grief has been widely related to a variety of illnesses (11). In summary, therefore, we expected the four groups to show the following declining levels of illness: 3–2–1–4 or 2–3–1–4 (see Table 4). Analysis of covariance, controlling for the same covariates as in the prior analyses, did find a significant difference among the groups ($p < .01$). Although the ranking of 2–4–1–3 closely matched one of our hypothesized rankings, a subsequent multiple range test indicated that ranking was primarily attributable to the low illness scores among those subjects scoring low on both grief scales (Group 1). None of the other group differences was significant ($p < .05$) according to the multiple range analysis. Apparently, we were premature in concluding that those scoring low on both Parts I and II would manifest somatic grief through moderate physical illness. On the other hand, the data are quite consistent with Parkes' finding that low levels of initial distress are often associated with low levels of later distress as well (7, 12).

The unexpected finding of lower illness scores where grief is least actually simplifies clinical interpretation of the TRIG. Using the norms depicted in Figure 1, the TRIG user can direct his or her questioning both to present and past adjustment patterns. Current levels of physical illness and past attendance at the deceased's funeral are just two of many areas yet to be tested.

CONCLUSION

The Texas Revised Inventory of Grief is a brief, readily interpretable, paper-and-pencil test for assessing grief. It is easily scored and scores can be compared with normative data for various time points following the death of a loved one. Quantifying past as well as present experiences, the TRIG offers a dynamic assessment of the grief process. As a clinical tool, the TRIG appears useful in identifying deviant grief reactions and measuring changes over time. As a research tool, it can help to establish clinical norms for the general population as well as for various socioeconomic groups, types of losses, different relationships, and so on, and might even help to unravel the complex relationship between immediate postbereavement behaviors (for example, life disruption or attending the funeral) and later outcomes (for example, intrusive memories, crying, nonacceptance, morbidity, or mortality). Thus, in both the clinical and the scientific environments, the TRIG may be a useful, practical, and reliable aid to measure grief.

REFERENCES

1. Faschingbauer TR, DeVaul RA, Zisook S: Development of The Texas Inventory of Grief. Am J Psychiatry 134:696-698, 1977
2. Hull CH, Nie NH: Statistical Package for Social Sciences (SPSS). New York, McGraw-Hill, 1975
3. Guttman L: Some necessary conditions for common factor analysis. Psychometrika 19:149-161, 1954
4. Faschingbauer TR: Texas Revised Inventory of Grief Manual. Houston, Honeycomb Publishing, 1981
5. Lord F, Novick M: Statistical Theories of Mental Test Scores. Reading, MA, Addison-Wesley, 1968
6. Chafetz JS: Masculine, feminine or human. Itasca, Ill, FE Peacock Publishers, 1978
7. Shweder RA: Illusory correlation and the MMPI controversy. J Consult Clin Psychol 45:917-924, 1977
8. Parkes CM, Weiss RS: Recovery from Bereavement. New York, Basic Books, 1983
9. Zisook S, Shuchter SR: Time course of spousal bereavement. Gen Hosp Psychiatry 7:95-100, 1985
10. Wyler A, Masuda M, Holmes T: The seriousness of illness rating scale. J Psychosom Res 11:363-374, 1968
11. Klerman GL, Izen JE: The effects of bereavement and grief on physical health and general well-being. Adv Psychosom Med 9:63-104, 1977
12. Glick IO, Weiss RS, Parkes CM: The First Year of Bereavement. New York, John Wiley and Sons, 1974

Chapter 8

Measures of the Psychological Distress of Bereavement

Selby C. Jacobs, M.D.

Chapter 8

Measures of the Psychological Distress of Bereavement

Until recently, the strategy for assessing the psychological response to loss was to use symptom checklists derived from concepts of psychopathology (1–5). These assessments usually did not focus on psychological phenomena associated with stress and were nonspecific in regard to the stimulus or cause of the distress. Recently, more specific psychometric instruments for the assessment of the psychological impact of bereavement have been developed (6–15). These instruments differ with respect to their theoretical framework, the scope of the psychological impact that is assessed, the specificity of the items for bereavement, and the samples in which they were developed and for which normative data are available.

DESCRIPTION OF THE MEASURES

The Impact of Event Scale (IES) is a self-report schedule of 15 items developed by Horowitz and colleagues that is intended to assess two major response sets of persons under various traumatic stresses, including bereavement (7). One response set, intrusion, is characterized by intruding thoughts and strong waves of affect. The other response set, avoidance, is characterized by ideational constriction and emotional blunting. These items are designed for assessment of the distress associated with traumatic events other than bereavement. The items are scored on the frequency of endorsement during the preceding week, and provide a rating of the intensity of the two response sets that are considered relevant to many different traumatic situations. The IES assesses information processing, cognition, and defense, but is limited in assessing the emotional, symptomatic, and motivational aspects of stress response. For example, no items from the IES address depressive phenomena. Among the four assessments to be discussed, the IES is relatively nonspecific for bereavement by comparison with the other three, all of which were developed uniquely for the assessment of loss or threatened loss.

These items were originally developed using a sample of 16 men and 50 women who were literate patients between 20 and 75 years of age, with a mean age of 34. All of them had traumatic neuroses. Approximately one-half of them had experienced bereavement. They came from diverse ethnic backgrounds, of middle and lower middle socioeconomic status, and lived in a large metropolitan area. A subsequent cross-validation study was completed on a sample of 35 outpatients and 37 field subjects equally divided between men and women who had experienced parental bereavement. The patient group that had a mean age of 31 was assessed 26 weeks, on the average, after the loss. The field subjects who had a mean age of 38 were assessed 8 weeks, on the average, after the loss. Both groups were of middle class socioeconomic status. Normative data are available on the original 66 subjects, an additional 75 male and 35 female medical students from the same area, and the sample of the cross-validation study.

The Texas Inventory of Grief (TIG) developed by Faschingbauer and colleagues is intended to assess unresolved aspects of the emotional response to the death of a close friend or relative (8). The seven self-report items of this inventory are designed to indicate the presence of unresolved grief. In this sense, it is highly specific and narrow in scope. The items in the TIG identify the persistence of emotional upset, preoccupations with the person who is gone, identificatory phenomena, the survivor's inability to accept the death, and anniversary distress. The items are rated on a graded true-false continuum (Likert-type) and provide a score for the intensity of unresolved grief. Object relations theory is probably the most important single theoretical basis for the inventory, but the authors draw on many theoretical views.

Recently, Zisook and colleagues reported on an inventory of 59 items expanded from the TIG for assessing a wide range of emotional, behavioral, and symptomatic phenomena (9). Item analyses have been completed on the 59 items. They are reported in Chapter 7 of this book and summarized in a manual that is available from the authors (10). In these analyses two sets of items emerged, including eight items on past behavior characterizing the individual adjustment to the loss and 13 items on present feelings. These 21 items are incorporated into the Texas Revised Inventory of Grief (TRIG).

The TIG has passed through at least two steps in development and the samples used vary somewhat. It was originally developed on 57 psychiatric outpatients with a mean age of 37.3 years and a mean education of 11.5 years that included 44 women and 13 men. All had experienced a death in the family. Subsequent development included an additional 211 bereaved subjects solicited by mail from the entire United States. They were middle class, well educated, 65 percent white, 62 percent women, and ranging in age from 19–74 years with a mean age of 36.5. Normative data are not broken down by age or sex and are only presented for four periods of grief extending over 10 years.

Another instrument is the self-report Grief Experience Inventory (GEI) developed by Sanders and colleagues specifically for the assessment of grief (11, 12). These investigators drew eclectically on several theoretical approaches and conceptualized grief as a multidimensional, evolving experience. The inventory of 135 true-false items is specific for bereavement and extensive in the phenomena assessed, including "experiences, feelings, symptoms, and behaviors." A manual available from the authors summarizes item analyses that identify nine subscales including despair, anger and hostility, guilt, social isolation, loss of control, rumination, depersonalization, somatization, and death anxiety (12).

These items were developed on two samples. The first sample was a group of 135 subjects who were bereaved in the past year and was composed of 114 college student volunteers, 10 bereaved volunteers from the community, and 11 members of a Golden Age club. The second sample was 102 recently bereaved persons identified through obituaries, and included 26 men and 76 women who had experienced the loss of a parent, spouse, or child. Their average age was 52. They were all white, and 39 percent had completed high school and another 35 percent, college. Normative data are available for both bereaved groups (12).

The bereavement items (BI) reported by Jacobs and colleagues include 18 new items on grief supplemented by the 20 items of the Center for Epidemiological Studies–Depression Scale (CES–D) (13, 14) that were developed for the assessment of grief within the framework of attachment theory (15–17). They are self-report items designed to assess emotional numbness-disbelief, separation anxiety (the pangs of grief and the perceptual changes of grief), and depressive symptoms that are scored according to frequency of occurrence in the past week. With the exception of the CES–D items, in particular the positively phrased ones and the items that assess negative attitudes, these items are specifically designed to assess the distress of bereavement. The BI is designed for use at any time in the course of bereavement. Item analyses identified dimensions within the total 38 items that correspond to the theoretically determined choice of items. That is to say, four dimensions emerged: numbness-disbelief;

sadness, loneliness, and crying; distressful yearning; and perceptual set and searching.

The sample used in the development of these items was 114 bereaved spouses who had experienced a loss one month earlier. Sixty-one percent were women; the mean age was 62.5; 28 percent had a high school education; and 85 percent were married only once. They were representative of a systematic sample from a metropolitan area. Normative data broken down by age and sex had been published for these items (16).

DISCUSSION OF THE MEASURES

No studies have empirically compared the measures to each other. For the purpose of choosing a particular measure, comparisons must therefore be made at present on the basis of an examination of the suitability of the items from each measure for the particular purposes of the investigator, and the efficiency of the measure in terms of length and ease of administration. More or less normative data are available for all the measures as indicated in the description of each measure.

Comparison of Content

Of the four measures that are available for the assessment of the distress of bereavement, the original TIG of seven items is the most limited in scope. It includes items on identification symptoms, acceptance of the death, and anniversary distress that are unique in assessing manifestations of unresolved grief presumed to be important from clinical work with bereaved persons. No other measures include these items. The remaining items reflect separation distress and are similar in content to some of the IES items on intrusion, the GEI items on loss of control and rumination, and the BI items on separation distress. This original version of the TIG is suitable for use only after the first anniversary of a loss is past. The TRIG (revised inventory) of 21 items introduces new items to assess family, social, and work adjustment after the death that are included in the set of items on "past behavior," two items on anger and irritability over the death, and a number of items that amplify assessment of the same dimensions already identified in the short version. This later version may be used at any point in the course of grief.

The IES assesses two dimensions of distress that are relevant at any time in the course of bereavement—intrusion and avoidance. Although not specifically designed for the purpose, the items on intrusion appear to assess separation distress as many items on the TIG do. The eight avoidance items tap a dimension not identified in the TIG. Two of these items denoting numbness of feeling and disbelief are similar to BI items on numbness-disbelief and GEI items on depersonalization; however, the rest characterize a conscious attempt to suppress emotion or cognition related to the event. These items are unique to the IES.

The BI contributes two new dimensions of assessment beyond what has already been discussed. One dimension is assessed by six items on perceptual set and searching for the deceased person. Two items from the IES on intrusion have a resemblance to these items. Sadness, loneliness, and crying is another dimension that is assessed in a more systematic fashion in the BI. Many items from the GEI on despair, guilt, social isolation, and somatization are relevant for this assessment; however, no other measure assesses the normal sadness and loneliness that is commonly observed during bereavement in such a coherent manner. As part of the assessment of depression, the BI includes five items on the neurovegetative symptoms of depression, two items reflecting interpersonal sensitivity to rejection, an item related to despair, and another to disturbance of self-esteem. Assessment of these dimensions of the distress of bereavement is developed to a greater extent in the last measure, the GEI.

The GEI, with 135 items, is by far the most extensive assessment of bereavement. In addition to the assessment of numbness, shock, and separation distress, including the pang of grief and searching, the GEI introduces several additional dimensions. These include despair, anger-hostility, guilt, social isolation, somatization, and death anxiety. Aside from a few items on anger and irritability in the TIG, and a limited number of items from the BI on each of despair, guilt, and somatization, no other measures reflect these dimensions of bereavement.

Specificity of Measurement for Bereavement

The items from the BI on distressful yearning, which is one of the hallmarks of the pang of grief, appear to be useful in assessment of distress associated with a threatened loss (15) and in this sense are nonspecific for bereavement. Actual bereavement and anticipatory grief, if that is what is being measured in the case of threatened loss, are sufficiently close in relationship to make this nonspecificity understandable.

The CES–D was originally developed for primary screening of depression in the community and is obviously nonspecific for bereavement in this regard (13, 14). This nonspecificity creates problems of application to a bereaved population. In particular, the positively phrased items, included in the CES–D as a test of "yea-saying," are considered inappropriate by many bereaved persons. Also, the few items on despair, self-esteem, and sensitivity to interpersonal rejection are not only quite limited in number but also did not appear as relevant to bereaved persons (reflected in low endorsement rates) as the other items on mood and neurovegetative symptoms, in part because of insufficient specificity of content for bereavement (15).

The issue of specificity also arose in the use of two separate measures of anxiety in unpublished studies done using the BI. Neither the items on anxiety from the Psychiatric Evaluation Research Interview (items considered to be nonspecific measures of psychological distress in the general population) (18), nor the Taylor Manifest Anxiety Scale (including items for rating anxiety in psychiatric patients) (19), were sensitive to group differences between bereaved and nonbereaved or were found to change over time. Furthermore, neither scale correlated significantly with the measure of separation distress.

Among the other measures, the IES is relatively nonspecific for the assessment of bereavement insofar as it is applicable to a wider range of potentially traumatic experiences. This nonspecificity does not appear to be problematic, however, as the IES was successfully used in that part of Horowitz's original sample that was bereaved and was subsequently used in a study of parentally bereaved adults. This may be a function of the close relationship between the distress of trauma and the distress of loss.

Psychological Dimensions of Grief

The development of these specific measures of the psychological distress of bereavement contributes to a concept of grief that includes multiple dimensions of distress that evolve somewhat independently over time. This is consistent with a contemporary formulation based on intensive follow-up on a small number of bereaved women (20). For example, separation anxiety and its associated symptoms, manifest in the classical pang of grief, ordinarily are intrusive early in the course of grief and then subside. Avoidance can be conspicuous at any time and, in particular, in the initial stages of grief when grief is frequently associated with emotional numbness. Manifestations of despair, depressive mood, and disorganization of routine behavior patterns tend to reach peak intensity later in the course of acute grief and precede recovery. Not every bereaved person follows the same pattern or time course of distress. Rather, the timing of peak intensity for single dimensions varies, the sequence of peak intensity for the various dimensions varies, single dimensions may have sub-peaks of intensity, and the timing of global intensity varies. No studies have yet tested hypotheses about the evolution of emotional distress over time as it is described here. Nevertheless, the availability of measures now makes it possible to explore such hypotheses in careful longitudinal studies of acutely bereaved subjects.

Furthermore, hypotheses about relationships among dimensions can now be explored. It is conceivable that when one dimension of grief is prominent, other dimensions of grief are less important or less likely to be reported. Taking numbness and disbelief from the BI as an example, such a proposition about the nature of the distress makes sense if numbness and disbelief are understood as an effort by the bereaved individual to maintain control and to defend against the overwhelming, immediate reality. A defensive effort of this sort may be incompatible with the deeper cognitive acceptance of the loss that underlies the expression of separation anxiety or the acceptance of the finality of the loss that underlies sadness, despair, and disorganization of behavior. In fact, analyses of the BI indicate that the items on numbness-disbelief correlate positively with the items on separation distress ($r = .61$) and share approximately one-third of their variance. Hence, a simple inverse, linear relationship does not exist although it may still be true at higher thresholds of emotional distress. Another, closely related example of interrelationships between dimensions is discussed in a later section of this chapter, entitled "Coping."

Atypical or Pathological Grief

One of the most important questions in bereavement research is whether atypical or pathological patterns of grief are associated with a higher risk of complications, both physical illness and mental disorders. Adequate studies to test this question are lacking in the literature. Perhaps the greatest limitation in approaching the issue has been the absence of a systematic assessment of atypical grief. The availability of the existing measures may help to tackle this problem; however, additional effort is needed to demonstrate this.

Given our present state of knowledge, it is reasonable to consider pathological grief as a manifestation of personality impairment involving attachment to and separation from significant others (21). This type of impairment may be reflected in a person's cognitive functioning (22), ego defenses (21, 23, 24), latent self-images and role relationships (25), and the integration of personality functioning (21, 26), not to mention a wide range of clinical presentations (27, 28) during acute bereavement. This impairment is also reflected in the nature of the separation distress evoked by a loss, specifically its intensity and course. Beginning with Lindemann (27, 29), description and classification of pathological grief have centered around this dimension (intensity and course) and defined three variants. One is delayed grief, in which separation distress is slow to emerge. In some instances, grief is absent over an extended period of time. Another variant is unusually severe or "distorted" grief, in which separation distress is overwhelming. The third variant is prolonged grief, in which distress over the loss is not satisfactorily resolved.

Of the measures available, the one that most directly purports to assess one dimension of atypical grief, that is to say unresolved grief, is the original TIG. As already noted, it is constructed around several items that reflect separation distress. One item in this measure that inquires about the anniversary of the loss limits the use of the full scale, including that item, during the first year of bereavement. Whether, in fact, the TIG would be effective in measuring the vicissitudes of separation anxiety in the first year of bereavement has not been tested. Subscales of the other measures, the IES intrusion scale, the GEI's rumination and loss of control scales, and the BI separation anxiety items might equally serve the same purpose. The development of assessments for use early in the course of bereavement is essential for the purpose of prompt identification of risk for complications.

In addition, the use of assessments for other dimensions of grief may prove useful. Anger and protest, which theoretically should correlate highly with separation distress, might characterize an aspect of distorted grief (21, 29). Similarly, despair and guilt may be dimensions of grief that are associated with unresolved grief in conjunction with prolonged depressions (30). The GEI provides subscales on these dimensions that need further testing.

Yet another dimension of the experience that has never been systematically assessed and may be useful is the degree to which and the duration that the bereaved person experiences fear and a prolonged state of alarm over the loss. The absence of a significant other person may sufficiently undermine the security of the survivor, and a severe state of agitation, if not anxiety disorder, may result if it goes unresolved (31). The GEI provides an assessment of death anxiety that may correlate with fear and arousal, but this remains a question for empirical study.

Finally, it is commonly believed that traumatic deaths are associated with more severe, problematic grief in the survivors. Untimely and unexpected deaths may be traumatic to some extent because of their nature, and certainly deaths from homicide, suicide, and accidents are traumatic as well as the cause of a loss. The trauma, the emotional states evoked by it, and the associated physiological changes may be critical dimensions of some experiences of loss that increase the risk of an atypical pattern of grief. Investigation of the relationship between the IES as a measure of distress that in part reflects this dimension and other assessments of grief may clarify this dimension.

Coping

It is commonly believed that certain coping styles are maladaptive during acute bereavement, yet with the exception of the IES subscale on avoidance and the GEI scale on social isolation (withdrawal), the rest of the measures are limited in the assessment of coping. These two aspects of coping—avoidance and social withdrawal, both if they are global and prolonged—in addition to vicarious care-giving in excess (32) and prolonged, frenetic hyperactivity (27), are the styles of presumed maladaptation that are most salient in the clinical literature. The interaction of this dimension of the human response to a loss with psychological distress needs further investigation. For instance, a positive correlation of a .42 was found between the intrusion and avoidance subscales of the IES in one sample, indicating that they shared about 16 percent of their variance (6). Hence, they were largely independent but nevertheless did not covary in a simple inverse relationship as might have been expected if one assumed that they would have a reciprocal relationship. In a subsequent study, the independence of the two subscales appeared to be a function of the severity of distress, the duration of the bereavement state, and treatment intervention, indicating the potential complexity of the relationship between these two parameters (7). Thus, when bereaved persons were less distressed and presumably modulating their distress with success, the magnitude of correlation was higher, ranging from .57 to .78. The development of more diversified assessments of coping will enhance the exploration of these important interactions.

Social Networks and Supports

Studies of the response of the family as a unit to the death of a member are quite limited (33). Nevertheless, this type of assessment and the interaction of psychological distress with the social supports may be equally as important as coping style as a determinant of the pattern of psychological distress.

Need for Additional Validation and Clinical Application

In the development of these measures of the psychological distress of bereavement, studies have been done to show that they discriminate between bereaved and nonbereaved and that they are sensitive to change over time. Additional validation is needed to establish the usefulness of the measures as substitutes for clinical judgments or ratings, both as correlates for biological changes associated with bereavement, and as predictors of outcome. For example, subscales of the BI have been correlated with clinical ratings of affect (34) and investigated with respect to several neuroendocrine parameters (see Chapter 9). In addition, the BI is currently being used in a longitudinal study of health outcomes and utilization of health services that will test its value as a predictor of healthy adaptation after the death of a spouse.

Such studies will establish a basis for the application of measures of the psychological distress of bereavement in clinical practice. Well-studied measures will be useful for identifying the minority of acutely bereaved persons who are at risk for prolonged unresolved grief and may make early interventions possible. These measures may also prove useful in the assessment of the depressive syndromes of bereavement to determine which of them are unlikely to remit spontaneously and require professional intervention (30).

REFERENCES

1. Maddison D, Viola A: The health of widows in the year following bereavement. J Psychosom Res 12:297-306, 1968
2. Wiener A, Gerber I, Bettin D, et al: The process and phenomenology of bereavement, in Bereavement: Its Psychosocial Aspects. Edited by Schoenberg B, Gerber I, Wiener A, et al. New York, Columbia University Press, 1975
3. Blanchard CG, Blanchard EB, Becker JV: The young widow: depressive symptomatology throughout the grief process. Psychiatry 39:394-399, 1976
4. Vachon MLS, Lyall WAL, Rogers J, et al: A controlled study of self-help intervention for widows. Am J Psychiatry 137:1380-1384, 1980
5. Clayton PJ: The bereavement of the widowed. Diseases of the Nervous System 32:597-604, 1971
6. Horowitz M, Wilner N, Alvarez W: Impact of event scale: a measure of subjective stress. Psychosom Med 41:209-218, 1979
7. Zilberg NJ, Weiss DS, Horowitz MJ: Impact of Event Scale: a cross-validation study and some empirical evidence supporting a conceptual model of stress response syndromes. J Consult Clin Psychol 50:407-414, 1982
8. Faschingbauer TR, DeVaul RA, Zisook S: Development of the Texas Inventory of Grief. Am J Psychiatry 134:696-698, 1977
9. Zisook S, DeVaul RA, Click MA: Measuring symptoms of grief and bereavement. Am J Psychiatry 139:1590-1593, 1982
10. Faschingbauer TR: Texas Revised Inventory of Grief manual. Houston, Honeycomb Publishing Company, 1981
11. Sanders CM, Mauger PA, Strong PN: Grief experiences inventory. Omega 10:303-322, 1979
12. Sanders CM, Mauger PA, Strong PN: A Manual for the Grief Experience Inventory. 1979
13. Comstock G, Helsing K: Symptoms of depression in two communities. Psychol Med 6:551-563, 1976
14. Weissman M, Sholomskas D, Pottenger M, et al: Assessing depressive symptoms in five psychiatric populations: a validation study. Am J Epidemiol 106:203-214, 1977
15. Jacobs S, Kasl S, Ostfeld A, et al: The measurement of grief: bereaved versus non-bereaved. The Hospice Journal (in press)
16. Jacobs S, Kasl S, Ostfeld A, et al: The measurement of grief: age and sex variation. Br J Med Psychol (in press)

17. Jacobs SC, Kosten TR, Kasl SV, et al: Attachment theory and multiple dimensions of grief. Omega (in press)
18. Dohrenwend BP, Shrout PE, Egri G, et al. Nonspecific psychological distress and other dimensions of psychopathology. Arch Gen Psychiatry 37:1229-1236, 1980
19. Taylor JA: A personality scale of manifest anxiety. J Abnorm Psychol 48:285-293, 1953
20. Parkes CM: The first year of bereavement. Psychiatry 33:444-467, 1970
21. Bowlby J: Attachment and Loss, vol. III: Loss. New York, Basic Books, 1980
22. Horowitz M, Wilner N, Kaltreider N, et al: Signs and symptoms of post-traumatic stress disorder. Arch Gen Psychiatry 37:85-92, 1980
23. Wolfe CT, Friedman SB, Hofer MA, et al: Relationships between psychological defenses and mean urinary 17-hydroxycorticosteroid excretion rates. Psychosom Med 26:576-591, 1964
24. Horowitz M: Stress Response Syndromes. New York, Jason Aronson, 1976
25. Horowtiz MJ, Wilner N, Marmor C, et al: Pathological grief and the activation of latent self-images. Am J Psychiatry 137:1157-1162, 1980
26. Deutsch H: Absence of grief. Psychoanal Q 6:12-22, 1937
27. Lindemann E: Symptomatology and management of acute grief. Am J Psychiatry 101:141-148, 1944
28. Anderson C: Aspects of pathological grief and mourning. Int J Psychoanal 30:48-55, 1949
29. Parkes CM: Bereavement: Studies of Grief in Adult Life. New York, International Universities Press, 1972
30. Jacobs S, Lieberman P: Bereavement and depression, in Presentations of Depression. Edited by Cameron OG. New York, John Wiley & Sons, 1986
31. Jacobs S: Bereavement and anxiety disorders, in Grief and Bereavement. Edited by Chigier E. Tel Aviv, Freund Publishing House, Ltd. (in press)
32. Bowlby J: Pathological mourning and childhood mourning. J Am Psychoanal Assoc 11:500-541, 1963
33. Kosten TR, Jacobs SC, Kasl SV: Terminal illness, bereavement and the family, in Health, Illness and Families: A Life Span Perspective. Edited by Turk DC, Kearns RD. New York, John Wiley & Sons, 1985
34. Jacobs SC, Kosten TR, Kasl SV, et al: A new bereavement scale (abstract). Proceedings of the 137th Annual Meeting of the American Psychiatric Association, Los Angeles, May 5-11, 1984

Chapter 9

Psychoendocrine Aspects of Bereavement

Selby C. Jacobs, M.D.

Chapter 9

Psychoendocrine Aspects of Bereavement

Although there have been a substantial number of studies on the psychoendocrinology of stress, the past 25 years have seen only two studies specifically examining the psychoendocrine aspects of bereavement: a study begun in the 1960s on the parents of leukemic children (1–4) and a study of bereaved spouses that will be summarized in this chapter (5–10).

In the first psychoendocrine study of bereavement, published in a series of papers in the mid-1960s and early 1970s, the investigators studied 17-hydroxycorticosteroid excretion in the parents both before and after the death of the child. Prior to this study, the psychoendocrine literature had emphasized the importance of emotional distress, emotional urgency, and emotional involvement for the prediction of adrenocortical activity (11–14). In the study of parents, the investigators, seeking an explanation of the observation that not all persons demonstrated adrenocortical activation in response to the stress of bereavement, reported that the effectiveness and style of ego defenses determined the level of 17-hydroxycorticosteroid output while the child was still alive (1, 2). Ego defenses were assessed by nonstructured, clinical judgment. In follow-up during bereavement, these variables did not explain variation in adrenocortical function. Rather, high ratings of "active mourning" and of the extent of "psychological defensive effort" were associated with high adrenocortical activity (3, 4). Some parents demonstrated a rise in adrenocortical activity after bereavement and others, a decline. Nonetheless, no group difference between before and after the loss was found, and levels of urinary 17-hydroxycorticosteroids were within a normal range in both phases of the study.

The second study involved bereaved spouses and spouses threatened with a loss due to life-threatening illness (5–10). This study sought to 1) confirm, if possible, the role of psychological defenses as mediating processes that would predict level of activity of several stress-responsive hormonal systems; 2) investigate the value of structured assessments of psychological distress both specific and nonspecific for bereavement in understanding the level of hormonal activity; and 3) use the hormonal data as predictive variables in the analysis of health status approximately one and two years after the stressful event. The longitudinal analyses are being reported for the first time in this chapter, as are the associations between separation anxiety and both cortisol (8) and growth hormone.

METHODS

Sixty-seven middle-aged and elderly persons, 43 of whom were widowed and the remaining 24 threatened with the loss of a spouse through life-threatening illness, were studied two months after either the loss or illness. The nonbereaved group was under considerable stress itself because of the severity of the spouse's illness. In addition to the index episode of illness, 8 (33%) of this group experienced the death of their spouse and another 7 (29%) experienced significant recurrence of the index illness or a secondary, serious illness of their spouse within four months after the psychoendocrine assessment. The procedure for assessment included an interview by a trained psychiatrist and the collection of blood and urine samples in relation to the interview. The actual number of subjects in specific analyses to be summarized below varied slightly as a function of the completeness of data collection for different variables (see Table 1). Several measures were used during the interview to evaluate personality variables: structured clinical assessments of ego defensive effectiveness (7); structured multiple-item indices of separation anxiety (15, 16); depression (15, 16); repressive defensiveness (5); and generalized anxiety (5). Psychoendocrine function was measured by standard, commercially available radioenzymatic assays of 24-hour urinary norepinephrine and epinephrine and radioimmunoenzymatic assays of 24-hour urinary free cortisol as well as serum cortisol, prolactin, and growth hormone taken before and again after the interview (5–10). In the longitudinal follow-up, 13 months and 25 months after the stressful event (11 months and 23 months, respectively, after the initial assessment), data on outcome were obtained through structured assessments of separation anxiety, depression, clinical and self-ratings of grief, number of visits to the doctor in the interval, number of days spent in the hospital, self-rated health, and mortality. As a general rule, no significant differences were found between the bereaved and nonbereaved on either the psychological or the endocrine parameters (see below, and Table 1). Therefore, the two groups were combined in the analyses of association between psychological and endocrine variables and the longitudinal analyses. This was done to make the sample size optimal. The details of methodology are available in previous papers (5–10).

Table 1. Summary of the Sample*

Variable	Bereaved (B)	Nonbereaved (NB)	Total
Age (±S.E.)	62 (±1)	61 (±1)	62
Sex (%F)	50	49	49
Medications (%)	23	17	21
Height/Weight	0.42	0.40	0.42
Exercise (%)[3]	23	35	27
Cigarettes (%)[3]	33	25	31
Alcohol use (%)	69	70	69
Caffeine (cups/day)[3]	3.3	3.4	3.3
Separation Anxiety (±S.E.)[1]	10.3 (±1.0)	6.8 (±1.5)	9.1
Depression (CES-D) (±S.E.)[4]	19.5 (±1.4)	18.6 (±2.0)	19.2
Urinary free cortisol μg/d (±S.E.)[2]	37.8 (±3.0)	33.9 (±3.0)	36.4
Serum cortisol change μg/dl, (±S.E.)[2]	0.76(±0.8)	0.80(±1.3)	0.77
Urinary epinephrine μg/d, (±S.E.)[3]	13.5 (±0.8)	12.0 (±0.9)	13.0
Urinary norepinephrine μg/d (±S.E.)[3]	53.8 (±3.2)	47.5 (±4.2)	51.6
Baseline serum prolactin ng/ml, (±S.E.)[4]	8.9 (±0.8)	10.0 (±1.9)	9.2
Serum prolactin change ng/ml, (±S.E.)[4]	0.19(±0.5)	−0.99(±0.6)	−0.16
Baseline serum growth hormone ng/ml, (±S.E.)[5]	1.5 (±0.4)	1.2 (±0.4)	1.4
Serum growth hormone change ng/ml, (±S.E.)[5]	0.06(±0.3)	−0.09(±0.4)	−0.01

*n = 67 (B = 43, NB = 24)
[1]n = 59, n(B)=41, n(NB)=18
[2]n = 63, n(B)=41, n(NB)=22
[3]n = 59, n(B)=39, n(NB)=20
[4]n = 54, n(B)=38, n(NB)=16
[5]n = 66, n(B)=39, n(NB)=27

RESULTS AND DISCUSSION

Psychological and Endocrine Relationships Two Months After a Loss or Threatened Loss

Ego Defenses. In the study of spouses facing an actual or threatened loss, ego defenses had no demonstrated association with level of adrenocortical activity (7). Thus, the findings of the study of parents which was based on nonstructured, clinical judgment obtained from multiple contacts with the parents (1, 2) could not be confirmed in the study of spouses using more structured and demonstrably reliable methodology in a limited exposure to the subjects consisting of one interview. While the absence of an association in the study of spouses may be seen as a function of a different methodology and a different sample, it is in fact consistent with the observations by Hofer and colleagues of the parents of leukemic children during bereavement (3, 4). On the other hand, several studies of other stressful experiences, including threatened loss, have concluded that ego defenses signicantly influence adrenocortical function (17–21).

This discrepancy is difficult to explain. It is conceivable that bereavement, by virtue of being a chronic and reasonably well defined stress, may be unique, and, hence, ego defenses may not have the same relationship to adrenocortical function in this circumstance. Nevertheless, there is reason to be skeptical about the validity of the explanation involving ego defenses and the literature that has grown up around it. The original study that employed unstructured, clinical judgments confounds assessment of affect with assessment of ego defenses (1, 2), and the rest of the literature is flawed by a tautology; that is, a propensity to equate low affective arousal with ego defensive effectiveness (19–21). Consequently, it is difficult to find convincing evidence that ego defenses determine the level of adrenocortical activity.

In the study of spouses, the relationship between ego defenses and other hormonal systems including catecholamines, growth hormone, and prolactin was also investigated. In general, no association was found. Only a structured measure of repressive defensiveness was useful in conjunction with the level of generalized anxiety in explaining growth hormone response (5).

Moving beyond the main implication of the study of parents of leukemic children, observations of psychological distress and endocrine parameters were made in a study of spouses that is interesting and worthy of further attention.

Cortisol. No difference between widowed and nonbereaved spouses was found in urinary free and serum cortisol (7, 8). The cortisol values for the entire sample fell within a normal range. Serum cortisol response (defined as a rise of greater than 3 μg/100 cc) over the course of the interview was not associated with any measures of psychological distress (7). On the other hand, two interesting findings emerged using 24-hour urinary free cortisol as a criterion. Those persons—those bereaved as well as those threatened with a loss—who had worsening separation distress over the month before our assessment (two months after the event) had not only higher levels of separation anxiety (8) but also had higher rates of free cortisol output than those whose separation anxiety was diminishing (8). This observation is consistent with the one previous study of bereavement (3, 4) and early psychoendocrine studies of adrenocortical function during stress (11–14). It is important to note that measures of separation distress isolated in time—that is, point measures at one month and two months after intake—did not correlate with urinary free cortisol (8). In addition to the association between the course of separation anxiety and urinary free cortisol, a significant positive correlation between age and urinary free cortisol excretion was found among persons with high depression scores ($r = .62, p<.01$) (6).

No dexamethasone suppression tests (DSTs) were done on the sample of 67 spouses. However, an independent study completed a small series of DSTs in 13 bereaved persons who had depressive syndromes 6 months after bereavement (22). All of the subjects suppressed by 4 P.M. after 1 mg of dexamethasone given at 11 P.M. the evening before. Interestingly, post-dexamethasone cortisol levels correlated with depression scores ($r = .59, p<.05$), a phenomenon observed in some studies of depressed patients (23, 24). On reviewing the literature, two other studies of acutely bereaved subjects one month or less after the death were found (25, 26). In these studies a 10–20 percent rate of nonsuppression was observed that was associated with anxiety scores, not depression.

Although these findings are still fragmentary, they permit a preliminary, tentative formulation of adrenocortical function during bereavement that is consistent with the early psychoendocrine literature (11–14). Nothing in the data suggests that bereavement as a stress is unique in quality or quantity of adrenocortical activity, at least by comparison with threatened loss, with the possible exception of ego defenses in the circumstances of anticipatory bereavement. The evidence does suggest that hypothalamo-pituitary adrenocortical (HPA) dysregulation may occur in a small proportion of acutely bereaved persons early in the course of bereavement. At this time, it is not possible to say whether this dysregulation is related to higher urinary free cortisol output. The dysregulation does not appear to be related to depression, but an age related increase in HPA function occurs in bereaved persons who are depressed. This age related change in HPA function in bereaved persons with high levels of depression is consistent with one other study (27). It can be speculated that this observation is related to subsensitivity of glucocorticosteroid receptors in the hypothalamus and pituitary of the elderly (28, 29) in interaction with stress related activation of the adrenal cortex.

It appears that worsening separation distress early in the course of grief (as well as under the stress of threatened loss) is associated with high adrenocortical activity and higher levels of separation distress. Parallel to this, nonsuppression on the DST appears to be associated with the degree of anxiety or separation distress.

Urinary Catecholamines. The study of catecholamines during stress and particularly during bereavement has lagged behind research involving the HPA system primarily because of technical problems in the measurement of catecholamines (30–32). Nevertheless, there is little doubt that both epinephrine and norepinephrine belong to the category of hormones which are responsive to psychological influences (30–32). Epinephrine response reflecting adrenal medullary activity has been associated with novel, unpredictable situations, emotional arousal, and a variety of emotions. Norepinephrine response reflecting primarily sympathetic nervous system activity has been associated with attention-demanding as well as unpleasant situations, physical activity, and, in early studies, expressed aggression (30, 33), although the selective association with aggression has been disputed (32). The literature indicates that catecholamine responses, in particular norepinephrine, occur at a higher psychological threshold than that for cortisol and do not adapt as rapidly as the cortisol response to chronic stress. Catecholamines may therefore be persistently elevated in circumstances of chronic stress (31).

With this background, 24-hour urinary epinephrine and norepinephrine output was studied in the same subjects as those described above who were under the chronic stress of either spousal bereavement or the threatened loss of a spouse (9). Twenty-four-hour urinary output of norepinephrine and epinephrine during bereavement was higher than normative values in the literature, but it was not associated with depression scores. Again, no differences were found between those who had experienced an actual loss two months earlier and those who were threatened with a loss (see Table 1). No relationships between indices of psychological distress, including a measure of anger, and catecholamine output were observed. Finally, it was found that older age was associated with higher levels of urinary norepinephrine and epinephrine output among bereaved subjects (norepinephrine: $r = .46, p<.01$; epinephrine: $r = .35, p<.05$).

This evidence indicates that activity of the sympathetic adrenomedullary system is high during acute bereavement. This activity does not appear to be related to depression scores, a somewhat surprising finding given the reports in the literature on higher secretion or higher levels of serum norepinephrine in depressed patients (34, 35). One possible explanation is that the stress of bereavement overrides the effects of depression on catecholamine systems. Alternatively, the sadness of bereavement is not the same as clinical depression. The positive correlation between age and catecholamines suggests that the sympathetic adrenal medullary system's adaptation to the chronic stress may be slower among elderly persons who are bereaved than among middle-aged counterparts. This conclusion is consistent with the nature of bereavement as a chronic stress, and other research that has shown that older human subjects have not only higher arterial blood pressure and plasma norepinephrine responses to stress (36) but also have slower recovery after even mild stress (37). Animal studies have also documented that norepinephrine depletion and time of recovery from stress are greater in older animals than younger controls (38).

Serum Prolactin. Although it is well established that prolactin production occurs in relation to psychological stress, little is known about the specific psychological mechanisms which underlie such responses, particularly in humans. A relationship between high scores on the Taylor Manifest Anxiety Scale and increases in prolactin during the premenstrual period have been reported (39). Another study found prolactin responses to a stressful mirror drawing test in "neurotically" anxious and depressed females, but not in neurotic men or controls (40, 41). Clinical observations of patients with various disorders strongly suggest that changes in prolactin are linked to depressed and irritable mood (42). These findings indicate that there may be multiple, interacting psychological factors which together determine prolactin responses to stress in the human.

Again, as can be seen in Table 1, no differences between bereaved and nonbereaved spouses were observed (omitting nonmenopausal women), and the two groups were combined, as before, for subsequent analysis (10). Two measures of psychological distress, both separation anxiety ($r = .35$, p<.01) and depression ($r = .39$, p<.01), were directly correlated with prolactin response during a stressful interview, and both dimensions of psychological distress correlated with each other (r = .53). When the sample was stratified first by depression score and then by separation anxiety, a positive correlation between separation anxiety and prolactin response was found only in the highly depressed half of the sample (r = .32, p<.05), and a positive correlation between depression and prolactin response only in the highest quartile of intensity for separation anxiety (r = .49, p<.05).

This suggests that both depression and separation anxiety, each in conjunction with high levels of the other but not independently, rendered both the widowed and nonbereaved spouse more physiologically sensitive to distressing challenges such as a stressful interview. Alternatively, it may be that global distress above a certain threshold is associated with the degree of physiological response. Both these interpretations are consistent with the conclusions from the previous literature on nonbereaved individuals.

Serum Growth Hormone. Several studies have demonstrated that some individuals have an elevation in serum growth hormone (HGH) in response to acute stress (43–45). These stress responders have been identified by clinical evaluations and by psychological tests as anxious or "neurotic." However, the trait of high anxiety alone is not sufficient to characterize these responders. In each study a different label has been given to a second factor, coupled with anxiety, which identifies responders. In short, the literature suggests that anxiety in conjunction with "neuroticism," or the psychological defensiveness measured by the K scale of the Minnesota Multiphasic Personality Inventory" (MMPI), or the clinical assessment of "nonengagement," can identify HGH responders to acute stress.

In the study of bereaved spouses and spouses threatened with a loss, the combined use of the Taylor Manifest Anxiety Scale and a measure of repressive defensiveness (the Crowne Marlowe) in a discriminant function analysis improved the ability of either scale alone to distinguish growth hormone responders (> 2.0 ng/ml from nonresponders) (5). Seventy-three percent of nonresponders and 70 percent of responders were correctly classified (p<.005). This observation was consistent with previous studies (43–45). Specific measures of the psychological distress of bereavement such as separation anxiety used as point measures at the time of the interview when growth hormone was assayed did not correlate with growth hormone response. However, in a group of subjects (n(B) = 16, n(NB) = 8) for whom separation anxiety was worsening in the month before the assay, the number of responders (B = 50 percent, NB = 63 percent) was significantly higher than in a group for whom the distress was subsiding (B = 36 percent, NB = 15 percent, χ^2, linear trend = 8.5, $p<.005$). This pattern was similar to the one observed for psychological distress and urinary free cortisol. Also, parallel to the other hormonal systems, no differences between the bereaved and nonbereaved were observed (see Table 1).

Longitudinal Analyses. Cross-sectional studies of the correlation between parameters of psychological distress and endocrine parameters may document co-variation in these but cannot address the question of whether such changes, either psychological or endocrine, increase the risk of illness and, therefore, presumably play a pathogenic role. The epidemiological literature encourages a search for risk factors by indicating that many bereaved persons, depending on age, sex, and other factors, are at risk for a reduced sense of well-being, nonspecific symptoms, and increased morbidity and mortality (including unresolved grief and depressive states) (46–48). To address these issues, we followed our sample longitudinally. The data for longitudinal analysis were limited by the small number of the original sample (n = 67), the reduced number that completed follow-up at 25 months (n = 52), and incomplete data collection on some parameters as mentioned under Methods.

Two previous studies show the potential value of using endocrine parameters in longitudinal studies. One prospective psychoendocrine study of stress related hormonal changes prior to onset of respiratory infections in army recruits revealed that subjects destined to become ill showed a greater percentage of extremely high or extremely low levels of cortisol, thyroxine, androsterone, and etiocholanolone about a week prior to illness as compared with control subjects (49). Other investigators reported a similar finding: both high and low levels of corticosteroids and etiocholanolone distinguished women at risk of having breast cancer from a control group in a prospective study (50).

With this background and with the cross-sectional analyses summarized above as a guide, longitudinal analyses were done with particular questions in mind. These included: 1) whether high urinary free cortisol or growth hormone response at two months of bereavement would predict a higher risk of unresolved grief; 2) whether high urinary catecholamines would predict poor outcomes, especially among the elderly; and 3) whether prolactin response would serve as a predictor. In general, these analyses did not support the hypotheses. Neither urinary free cortisol, urinary catecholamines, nor serum prolactin change values were significantly related to any of the outcomes including measures of persistent, intense grief, depression, illness behavior, illness episodes or mortality after six months, one year, and two years of bereavement. Next, having divided the sample into terciles on several endocrine parameters, including urinary free cortisol and urinary catecholamines, the longitudinal pattern of response to measures of psychological distress was plotted and tests of differences in means at specific points in time were completed. In general, these analyses revealed no differences among terciles that were independent of age and sex as factors. For example, at six months a linear trend between tercile of urinary free cortisol output and both separation anxiety and depression was observed: the highest tercile at two months after a loss or threatened loss predicted the highest level of distress. This finding was also true for urinary catecholamines with the exception that no gradient was observed from lowest tercile to highest. However, in a general linear models analysis, this linear trend was not independent of age and sex variation in the endocrine terciles. The number of visits to a doctor or clinic was also used as the criterion in such analyses and the endocrine parameters failed to predict this index of health services utilization. Curiously, a high NE/E ratio was associated with a high utilization of health services, although the meaning of the association is still obscure and may simply be Type I error, given the large number of analyses.

Based on these analyses, it must be concluded that neuroendocrine parameters do not serve as useful predictors of health outcomes for bereaved spouses and those threatened with a loss in the very small sample used in this longitudinal study. The data will be explored further using more complicated survival analyses and refined outcome criteria; however, the small number of subjects will limit the power of these analyses.

CONCLUSIONS

These observations of bereaved spouses and spouses threatened with a loss are consistent with the conclusion that bereavement evokes a response from endocrine systems that have been identified as stress responsive systems. A state of high physiological arousal is not found in everyone who is bereaved but rather is a function of the type, the degree, and the course over time of psychological distress. No evidence from this study supports the role of ego defenses as mediating psychological mechanisms for any of the endocrine systems that were studied, with the possible exception of serum growth hormone.

Bereavement as a stress does not appear to be more severe or unique in terms of endocrine physiology by comparison with threatened loss.

With full acknowledgement that a study as small as this cannot serve as a definitive test, no evidence is found in preliminary analyses that endocrine parameters predict illness outcomes, or that endocrine mechanisms are involved in psychiatric or medical complications of bereavement.

Finally, the application of these studies to clinical work is limited. No specific implication for practice with bereaved patients emerges from the data. Two main possibilities for further study stand out. One is related to the findings that a high level of adrenocortical activity and a growth hormone response to a stressful interview early in bereavement are associated with unremitting grief over the first two months of bereavement. Although these parameters do not predict subsequent outcome of the course of grief or health status in this sample, suggesting that these are normal manifestations of early bereavement, further investigation and development of these measures may prove to have some use in predicting who is at risk for the complications of bereavement such as unresolved grief or depressive states.

The other possibility involves clarification of the relationship between normal bereavement and the clinical complications that may arise. For example, some similarities between bereavement and depression emerge from these studies, such as evidence for increased adrenocortical activity, evidence for elevated adrenal medullary and sympathetic activity, the suggestion that the prolactin system may be activated, and the possibility that growth hormone dynamics are altered both in some bereaved subjects and in some depressed patients. However, these changes in bereaved persons are not associated directly and simply with scores on depression but rather are a function of multiple variables including age, separation anxiety, and perhaps defensiveness (at least for growth hormone) in complicated interactions.

Additional research is also necessary to follow leads in these studies to clarify the basic physiology of grief. More work directly comparing bereavement with psychopathological states and normal states needs to be done to help clarify the meaning of the physiological change that is observed in some bereaved persons. Additional measures of endocrine systems must be used, including receptor challenge tests, suppression tests, and repeated serum assays to determine the dynamics of the specific systems and the relationship of these dynamics to various indices of health. Finally, investigation of the selectivity of hormonal response and the use of multiple hormonal profiles may lead to means of defining risk for illness (51).

References

1. Wolff C, Friedman S, Hofer M, et al: Relationship between psychological defenses and mean urinary 17-hydroxycorticosteroid excretion rates, I: a predictive study of parents of fatally ill children. Psychosom Med 26:576-591, 1964
2. Wolff C, Hofer M, Mason J: Relationship between psychological defenses and mean urinary 17-hydroxycorticosteroid excretion rates, II: methodologic and theoretical considerations. Psychosom Med 26:592-609, 1964
3. Hofer M, Wolff C, Friedman S, et al: A psychoendocrine study of bereavement, I: 17-hydroxycorticosteroid excretion rates of parents following death of their children from leukemia. Psychosom Med 34:481-491, 1972
4. Hofer M, Wolff C, Friedman S, et al: A psychoendocrine study of bereavement, II: observations on the process of mourning in relation to adrenocortical function. Psychosom Med 34:492-504, 1972
5. Kosten T, Jacobs S, Mason J, et al: Psychological correlates of growth hormone response to stress. Psychosom Med 46:49-58, 1984
6. Jacobs S, Mason J, Kosten T, et al: Urinary free cortisol excretion in relation to age in acutely stressed persons with depressive symptoms. Psychosom Med 46:213-221, 1984
7. Jacobs S, Mason J, Kosten T, et al: Acute bereavement, threatened loss, ego defenses and adrenocortical function. Psychother Psychosom (in press)
8. Jacobs S, Mason J, Kosten T, et al: Acute bereavement, threatened loss, separation anxiety, and adrenocortical function. Manuscript available from author
9. Jacobs S, Mason J, Kosten T, et al: Bereavement and catecholamines. J Psychosom Res (in press)
10. Jacobs S, Brown S, Mason J, et al: Psychological distress, depression and prolactin response in stressed persons. J Human Stress (in press)
11. Bliss E, Migeon C, Branch C, et al: Reaction of the adrenal cortex to emotional stress. Psychosom Med 18:56-76, 1956
12. Fox H, Murawski B, Bartholomay A, et al: Adrenal steroid excretion patterns in eighteen healthy subjects. Psychosom Med 23:33-40, 1961
13. Price D, Thaler M, Mason J: Preoperative emotional states and adrenal cortical activity studies on cardiac and pulmonary surgery patients. AMA Archives of Neurology and Psychiatry 77:646-656, 1957
14. Mason JW: Psychological influences on the pituitary adrenocortical system. Recent Prog Horm Res 15:345, 1959

15. Jacobs S, Kasl S, Ostfeld A, et al: The measurement of grief: Bereaved versus non-bereaved. The Hospice Journal (in press)

16. Jacobs S, Kasl S, Ostfeld A, et al: The measurement of grief: age and sex variation. Br J Med Psychol (in press)

17. Katz J, Weiner H, Gallagher T, et al: Stress, distress and ego defenses, psychoendocrine response to impending breast tumor biopsy. Arch Gen Psychiatry 23:131-142, 1970

18. Katz J, Ackman P, Rothwax Y, et al: Psychoendocrine aspects of cancer of the breast. Psychosom Med 32:1-18, 1970

19. Bourne P, Coli W, Datel W: Affect levels of ten special forces soldiers under threat of attack. Psychol Rep 22:363-366, 1968

20. Bourne P, Rose R, Mason J: 17-OHCS levels in combat: special forces "A" team under threat of attack. Arch Gen Psychiatry 19:135-140, 1968

21. Rose R, Poe R, Mason J: Psychological state and body size of 17-OHCS excretion. Arch Intern Med 121:406-413, 1968

22. Kosten TR, Jacobs SC, Mason JW: The dexamethasone suppression test during bereavement. J Nerv Ment Dis 172:359-360, 1984

23. Holsboer F, Bender W, Benkert O, et al: Diagnostic value of dexamethasone suppression test in depression. Lancet 2:706, 1980

24. Carroll BJ, Feinberg M, Greden JD, et al: A specific laboratory test for the diagnosis of melancholia. Arch Gen Psychiatry 38:15-22, 1981

25. Das M, Berrios GE: Dexamethasone suppression test in acute grief reaction. Acta Psychiatr Scand 70:278-81, 1984

26. Shuchter SR, Zisook S, Kirkorowicz C, et al: The dexamethasone test in acute grief. Am J Psychiatry 143:879-881, 1986

27. Asnis G, Sachar E, Halbreich U, et al: Cortisol secretion in relation to age in major depression. Psychosom Med 43:235-242, 1981

28. Spar J, Gerner R: Does the dexamethasone suppression test distinguish dementia from depression? Am J Psychiatry 139:238-240, 1982

29. Brown W: Effect of age on DST results (letter). Am J Psychiatry 139:1376-1377, 1982

30. Mason J: A review of psychoendocrine research on the sympathetic–adrenal medullary system. Psychosom Med 30:631-651, 1968

31. Rose R: Endocrine responses to stressful psychological events. Psychiatr Clin North Am 3:251-276, 1980

32. Frankenhaeuser M: Experimental approaches to the study of catecholamines and emotion, in Emotions—Their Parameters and Measurement. Edited by Levi L. New York, Raven Press, 1975

33. Funkenstein D, King S, Drolette M: The direction of anger during a laboratory stress-inducing situation. Psychosom Med 16:404-413, 1954

34. Lake C, Pickar D, Ziegler M, et al: High plasma norepinephrine levels in patients with major affective disorder. Am J Psychiatry 139:1315-1318, 1982

35. Esler M, Turbott J, Schwarz R, et al: The peripheral kinetics of norepinephrine in depressive illness. Arch Gen Psychiatry 39:295-300, 1982

36. Palmer G, Ziegler M, Lake C: Response of norepinephrine and blood pressure to stress increases with age. J Gerontol 33:482-487, 1978

37. Faucheux BA, Bourliere F, Baulon A, et al: The effects of psychosocial stress on urinary excretion of adrenaline and in 51–55 and 71–74-year-old men. J Gerontol 27:313-325, 181

38. Ritter S, Pelzer N: Magnitude of stress-induced brain norepinephrine depletion varies with age. Brain Res 152:170-175, 1978

39. Halbreich U, Ben-David M, Assael M, et al: Serum prolactin in women with premenstrual syndrome. Lancet 2:654-656, 1976

40. Miyabo S, Asato T, Miyushima N: Prolactin and growth hormone responses to psychological stress in normal and neurotic subjects. J Clin Endocrinol Metab 44:947-951, 1977

41. Miyabo S, Hisada T, Asato T, et al: Growth hormone and cortisol responses to psychological stress: comparison of normal and neurotic subjects. J Clin Endocrinol Metab 42:1158-1162, 1976

42. De La Fuente J, Rosenbaum A: Prolactin in psychiatry. Am J Psychiatry 138:1154-1160, 1981

43. Greene WA, Conrow G, Schalch DS, et al: Psychological correlates of growth hormone and adrenal secretory responses to patients undergoing cardiac catheterization. Psychocom Med 32:599-614, 1970

44. Kurokawa N, Suematsu H, Tamai H, et al: Effect of emotional stress on human growth hormone secretion. J Psychosom Res 21:231-235, 1977

45. Miyabo S, Asato T, Miyushima N: Prolactin and growth hormone responses to psychological stress in normal and neurotic subjects. J Clin Endocrinol Metabol 44:947-951, 1977

46. Jacobs SC, Ostfeld AM: An epidemiological review of the mortality of bereavement. Psychosom Med 39:344-357, 1977

47. Jacobs SC, Douglas L: Grief: a mediating process between a loss and illness. Compr Psychiatry 20:165-175, 1979

48. Klerman G, Izen J: The effects of bereavement and grief on physical health and general well being. Adv Psychosom Med 9:63, 1977

49. Mason JW, Buescher EL, Belfer ML, et al: Pre-illness hormonal changes in army recruits with acute respiratory infections (abstract). Psychosom Med 29:545, 1967
50. Bulbrook RP, Haywood JL: Abnormal urinary steroid excretion and subsequent breast cancer. Lancet 1:7489, 1967
51. Mason JW: Emotion as Reflected in Patterns of Endocrine Integration, in Emotions—Their Parameters and Measurement. Edited by Levi L. New York, Raven Press, 1975

Chapter 10

Depressive Symptoms and Immune Function During Bereavement

Michael Irwin, M.D.
Herbert Weiner, M.D.

Chapter 10

Depressive Symptoms and Immune Function During Bereavement

The loss of a spouse is a tragic experience: it is accorded premier status of all adverse life experiences, rank-ordered in terms of their impact (1). Much of this book focuses on the psychological reactions that occur in conjugal bereavement. In addition, physiological changes occur during and after bereavement (2). In this chapter, we will add another dimension to the study of bereavement by describing changes in the immune system. We shall review clinical studies that indicate an association among bereavement, morbidity, and mortality. To account for this association, the hypothesis will be entertained that immune changes during and following bereavement may adversely influence health.

We begin with an introductory review of the main components of the immune system, and the manner in which they are assayed. Finally, we shall summarize several recent studies that have demonstrated an association between bereavement and changes in immune status. Also, the relation of depressive symptoms to these alterations in immune functions will be discussed.

HEALTH OUTCOME, DEPRESSIVE SYMPTOMS, AND BEREAVEMENT

Abundant observations have been recorded that the health of approximately 67 percent of widows declines within one year of bereavement (3-5), and that their medical (6-8) and psychiatric morbidity increases (9). Parkes, in a study of patients admitted to a psychiatric hospital, found that the number of patients whose illness followed the loss of a spouse was significantly greater than anticipated for people of that age and social group (9). Major depressions are particularly frequent in bereaved persons (9); in one study, 45 percent became severely depressed within one year after their loss (10). Such depressions enhance the risk of suicide, which then becomes another (but not the only) cause for the known increase in mortality observed in survivors six months after the loss (3, 11, 12).

Young and his colleagues (13), studying the mortality among widowers, found that 213 of 4486 widowers, 55 years old and older, died within the first six months of the loss of the spouse, an increase of about 40 percent above that expected for married men of the same age. Kraus and Lilienfield (14) noted that the mortality rate of persons of both sexes who had lost a spouse was increased and that there was a mortality in excess of that expected in those under 35 years of age. In a recent study, Helsing and colleagues (15) confirmed Young's observations and it is now clear that widowers between 55 and 74 years of age are considerably more likely to die.

Less believable to many physicians are the observations that losses are the circumstances in which major medical diseases begin. Schmale (16), postulating that object loss and depression are often the setting in which disease occurs, studied 42 patients admitted to a general medical service. Interviews documented that 31 of the 42 patients experienced the onset of an illness within one week of a significant loss. Developing Schmale's work in the area of giving up and its primary feelings of hopelessness and helplessness, Engel has hypothesized that the "giving-up, given-up complex" is the emotional setting in which most diseases occur (17).

In support of this hypothesis, several prospective studies have documented a relation between depression and morbidity (18). Kerr (19), in a four-year follow-up of patients with primary diagnoses of affective disorders, found a higher than expected mortality, particularly from carcinoma, in male patients over age 40 as compared to males of similar age in the general population. Varsamis (20) confirmed these observations in a six-year follow-up of psychiatric patients. Also, older patients (mean age 76.5 years) with affective disorders had a higher incidence of malignant disease as compared to other geriatric patients (21). Niemi (22) reported on cancer morbidity rather than mortality, and in affective disorder patients (mean age 46.7 years) found rather more men than women developed malignant disease, but that in this younger population the increased incidence was not statistically greater than in the general population. Such observations suggest that the association of depression and disease onset is in part age-dependent.

RELEVANCE OF IMMUNE CHANGES TO HEALTH OUTCOME

Our knowledge of the psychobiology of bereavement is limited. Therefore, we cannot as yet explain why the mortality of the bereaved is increased. One reason for increased mortality is that changes in the immune system may occur to account for an increase in infectious, neoplastic, and autoimmune disease. Presumably such changes are mediated by the brain (23) in a manner that is not yet apparent.

The relation among bereavement, reactions to it, immune function alterations, and health status are probably complex and largely unexplored. While immune changes may be relevant to morbid risk, it may be too simplistic to suggest that bereavement related decreases in one immune parameter may lead to increased illness susceptibility. For example, within the immune system itself, a decrease in one immune parameter, helper function, may result in an increased risk for acute viral infections, but decreased risk for autoimmune processes. Thus, an association between illness susceptibility and immune changes depends not only on the magnitude of immune change but also on the specific immune function involved. A review of the major components of the immune system and their relation to a variety of illnesses is presented in the following section.

THE IMMUNE SYSTEM

The immune system is a surveillance mechanism that discriminates "self" from "non-self" (24). Immune responses to foreign antigens protect the individual from disease-causing microorganisms such as bacteria and viruses, parasites, and cancer cells (25). This immune protection is provided by a dual system, the *cellular* and the *humoral immune responses* (26).

The humoral immune response leads to the production of antibody. The pathway of the humoral response involves complex interactions among several immune cells including T lymphocytes, B lymphocytes, and accessory cells. One kind of T lymphocyte, the T helper cell, responds to "non-self", presents the antigen, and interacts with B cells to trigger their differentiation and secretion of antibody. Deficiencies of any component in this pathway will lead to a diminished humoral response (a decreased response to non-self), and a decreased resistance to infection (26, 27). For example, loss of T helper cells occurs in individuals with acquired immunodeficiency syndrome and these persons become infected with viral, bacterial, fungal, and parasitic organisms (28, 29).

The cellular immune response is characterized by the ability of various killer cells to seek out and destroy cells that have acquired foreign "non-self" characteristics. Some of these killer cells interact with T helper cells to proliferate and, then, to kill specific foreign cells; whereas other killer cells demonstrate killer activity that is immunologically nonspecific (26, 30). These cells that are able to lyse a wide variety of cell types are called natural killer (NK) cells. Loss of killer cell function seriously impairs the body's defenses against tumor cells and viral infections (30, 31). Individuals deficient in the function of this system demonstrate a higher incidence of spontaneous tumors, particularly cancers of the hematolymphoid system. For example, persons with either congenital, drug induced, or acquired immunodeficiency syndromes (who have defective function of the cellular immune system) have up to an 80-fold increased risk of developing tumors (26).

A failure in the regulation of the immune response or a tendency to respond inappropriately can result in the production of antibodies directed against the self (24). These autoimmune responses may include the humoral and/or cellular immune responses, such as autoantibodies and killer T cells. These responses, which reflect the interaction of lymphocytes, are hypothesized to come about because helper T cells are induced or suppressor T cells are inhibited (32). Self-directed immune responses are characterized in a variety of disorders such as thyroiditis, rheumatoid arthritis, myasthenia gravis, and disseminated lupus erythematosus (26, 33).

MEASURES OF IMMUNE FUNCTION

A variety of clinical immunologic techniques are used to assess the immune function of an individual. These measures include the assessment of bone marrow production using the peripheral white blood count and tests of cellular and humoral immunity. Evaluation of cellular immunity involves delayed hypersensitivity skin tests, quantitation of T cells using specific markers, and nonspecific mitogen responses. The humoral system is evaluated using quantitative immunoglobulins and specific antibody responses after immunization.

APPLICATION OF IMMUNE MEASURES TO STUDIES IN BEREAVEMENT

Clinical studies of immune function in bereavement have, until recently, evaluated lymphocyte responses to mitogen stimulation (23, 34, 35). While lymphocyte stimulation is an in vitro correlate of cellular immune function, the measure represents the nonspecific proliferative response of either T or B cells to the artificial stimulants, concanavalin A, pokeweed mitogen, and phytohemagglutinin. Recent advances in immunology over the last decade have provided new techniques and methods that can be used in the clinical setting to assess specific alterations in cell-mediated immune function and, thus, extend the earlier observations. We are now able to characterize alterations in lymphocyte subsets, important in the regulation of immune responses, and to evaluate changes in the immune surveillance system.

With the development of monoclonal antibodies that characterize T cells, the number of T cells and their various subpopulations can be counted and identified. For example, specific antibodies, identified on T helper and T suppressor cells, quantitate the relative numbers of these regulatory cells. As mentioned above, relative deficiencies in T helper cells are associated with impaired humoral and cellular immune responses; whereas deficiencies of T suppressor cells are associated with autoimmune responses (24).

Another parameter of immune function is natural killer cell activity. This measure is an in vitro correlate of the immune surveillance system (31). The ability of killer cells to lyse tumor target cells is quantitatively measured by labeling the target cells with radioactivity, incubating the killer cells with the target cells, and then counting the released radioactivity (36, 37).

CHANGES IN IMMUNE FUNCTION IN BEREAVEMENT

Studies of Lymphocyte Responses to Mitogen Stimulation

Loss and bereavement appear to have significant effects on the immune system. Bartrop (34) studied the stimulation of phytohemagglutinin and concanavalin A (both mitogens) on the incorporation of thymidine into the lymphocytes of widows and an age-matched control population. Measures of lymphocyte responses to mitogen stimulation were compared in these two groups during the first month and again six to eight weeks after the death of the spouse. While no differences between the bereaved subjects and controls were demonstrated immediately after the bereavement, the bereaved women had significantly lower lymphoycte responses to mitogens than the control subjects two months later. This cross-sectional study was the first to document an alteration in immune function following bereavement, but it did not explore the presence of these altered lymphocyte responses before bereavement.

The effect of bereavement on the lymphocyte responses to mitogens was investigated in a second study (23). In this study, measures of mitogen responses were taken in men before and after the death of their spouse. Although the men had experienced the life difficulties associated with their spouse's terminal metastatic breast cancer, a significant suppression of lymphocyte responses only occurred subsequent to the spouse's death. These investigators concluded that the depressed lymphocyte responses did not occur in anticipation of bereavement but only following it.

The unfolding pattern of the suppression of lymphocyte stimulation following bereavement is not the same in the two studies cited. Schleifer and colleagues (23) reported measurable lymphocyte suppression within one month after bereavement, while Bartrop (34) did not find changes until after two months. Differences in study design, sex of the subjects, and/or their responses to bereavement may have contributed to these results.

Yet, these two studies documented an association between bereavement and changes in immune function and they raised new questions. Does bereavement not only affect lymphocyte responses to mitogens but, also, more specific, clinically relevant immune parameters? A demonstration of a relationship between bereavement and changes in specific immune parameters (such as killer cell activity or T cell subpopulations) would provide a more sophisticated assessment of the effects of bereavement on the immune system (35).

Second, do depressive symptoms mediate the suppression of immune function during bereavement? For example, cell mediated immune function appears to be impaired in depressed patients. Lymphocyte responses to mitogen stimulation, an in vitro correlate of cell-mediated immunity, are lower in hospitalized, depressed patients as compared to age-matched controls (38, 39). Because ambulatory depressed patients do not show similar decreases in mitogen responses, severity of depressive symptoms has been suggested (40) and more recently correlated with depressed mitogen responses (41).

Psychologic states may also mediate alterations of NK activity. Depressive and anxious symptoms are correlated with lower NK activity in students taking examinations (42) and in psychiatric inpatients (43). Locke and colleagues (44) have found that subjects who report both adverse life events and psychological symptoms (anxiety and depression) have lower NK immune function than subjects who report similar adverse events but have *few* symptoms.

We have conducted a series of studies that address the role of bereavement and depressive symptoms in altering T cell subpopulations and NK activity. The two studies to be reviewed below consist of 1) a cross-sectional comparison of NK activity and T cell subpopulations in bereaved and nonbereaved women who differed in the severity of their depressive symptoms; and 2) a longitudinal evaluation of depressive symptoms and NK activity in women during bereavement in order to determine whether the decrease in NK activity is a consequence of bereavement or the depressed mood state.

Changes in NK Activity and T cell Subpopulations

In the first study, immune function in a bereaved population was studied by comparing measures of NK activity, T cell subpopulations, and total lymphocytes in recently bereaved (less than six months) spouses (n = 10) and in nonbereaved controls (n = 8). The 18 women who composed the study population were free of chronic medical disorders associated with altered immune function; none was tested during the week after an episode of infectious disease. Because changes in nutrition (45), activity (46), and drug and alcohol use influence NK function (47), we excluded subjects who took drugs or alcohol and measured changes in weight and activity.

The subjects and controls were studied several times over a one- to three-month period and all were tested at least three times. At each testing the subject underwent a venipuncture at approximately the same hour to control for circadian effects and then met with a psychiatrist who rated depressive symptoms with the Hamilton Rating Scale for Depression (HDRS) (48). Immune measures were completed including total white blood cell count, T cell subpopulation enumeration by direct immunofluorescent monoclonal antibodies, and standard chromium assay of NK activity.

These particular immunologic measures are known to show considerable variation; therefore, multiple measures of each parameter were obtained to confirm the reproducibility of these determinations. Expression of these data as mean measures for each subject minimizes the influence of this variability in our comparison of bereaved and nonbereaved women.

The results are displayed in Table 1. The bereaved subjects were not different from controls in age or ethnic composition. To test formally for group differences on the dependent variables in question, simple *t*-tests were run.

Depressive symptoms were significantly elevated in the bereaved group as compared to the controls ($T = -3.17$, $df = 16$, $p < .003$). NK activity was significantly lower in the bereaved subjects than in the controls ($T = 1.9$, $df = 16$, $p = .04$) (Table 1 and Figure 1). The absolute number of lymphocytes were not significantly different in the two groups, nor were there group differences in T cell subpopulations including the variables percent of T helper, percent of T suppressor/cytotoxic cells, and the ratio of T helper to T suppressor/cytotoxic cells.

These findings demonstrate an impairment of NK activity in women who have experienced the death of their spouse as compared to immune function in women who are not bereaved. The impairment of NK activity in these bereaved subjects could not be accounted for by differences in health status, medication use, alcohol abuse, or weight changes. However, depressive symptoms, which have been associated with impaired NK activity by other investigators (42–44), were more severe in the bereaved group. The relation among depressive symptoms and alterations in NK activity and other immune variables was investigated using correlation procedures.

BEREAVEMENT, DEPRESSIVE SYMPTOMS, AND IMMUNE CHANGES

As already mentioned, other investigators have demonstrated that impaired mitogen responses are associated with depressive symptoms (38, 39). We assessed the strength of this relationship in our study population of 18 women by correlating severity of depressive symptoms with the immune parameters, NK activity, T cell subpopulations, and total lymphocyte count.

These results indicate that while an impairment of NK activity was related to dysphoric mood ($r = 0.49, p < .02$), it was not significantly correlated with the total HDRS scores.

Table 1. Age, Race, Depression Symptoms, and Immune Variables in Bereaved Subjects and Nonbereaved Controls

	Non-Bereaved (n=8)	Bereaved (n=10)	Significance
Measure	(group mean ± SD)		
Age (in years)	52.5 ± 9.5	57.1 ± 7.9	NS
Race			NS
white	6	8	
black	2	2	
HDRS	4.0 ± 4.9	12.5 ± 6.2	T=3.17, df 16, p=.003
NK activity (in lytic units)	36.4 ± 29.4	17.5 ± 10.5	F=1.9, df 16, p=.04
Total lymphocytes (cells/mL$^{x10^{-6}}$)	1.9 ± 0.6	2.5 ± 0.9	NS
% Th*	0.37 ± 0.07	0.37 ± 0.09	NS
% Ts**	0.31 ± 0.07	0.26 ± 0.10	NS
Th/Ts	1.35 ± 0.46	1.61 ± 0.40	NS

*Th = T helper cells
**Ts = T suppressor/cytotoxic cells

However, HDRS total scores were significantly associated with a relative loss of T suppressor/cytotoxic cells (r = 0.51, $p<.03$) and with an increase in the ratio of T helper to T suppressor/cytotoxic cells (r = 0.82, $p<.001$) (Figure 2). This increase in the ratio of T helper to T suppressor/cytotoxic cells was significantly correlated with all Hamilton subscales including depressed mood (r = .48, $p<.04$), insomnia (r = 0.55, $p<.02$), anxiety (r = 0.82, $p<.001$), and somatic symptoms (r = 0.65, $p<.005$). Neither T helper cells nor total lymphocyte counts were correlated with the severity of depressive symptoms.

These changes in the relative numbers of T suppressor/cytotoxic cells and in the ratio of T helper to T suppressor cells were within the normal range and do not necessarily have clinical significance. However, others have reported that clinically depressed patients have an increased incidence of autoantibodies (49, 50–52). It is also known that relative decreases in suppressor/cytotoxic cells are associated with an increased incidence of autoantibodies (32).

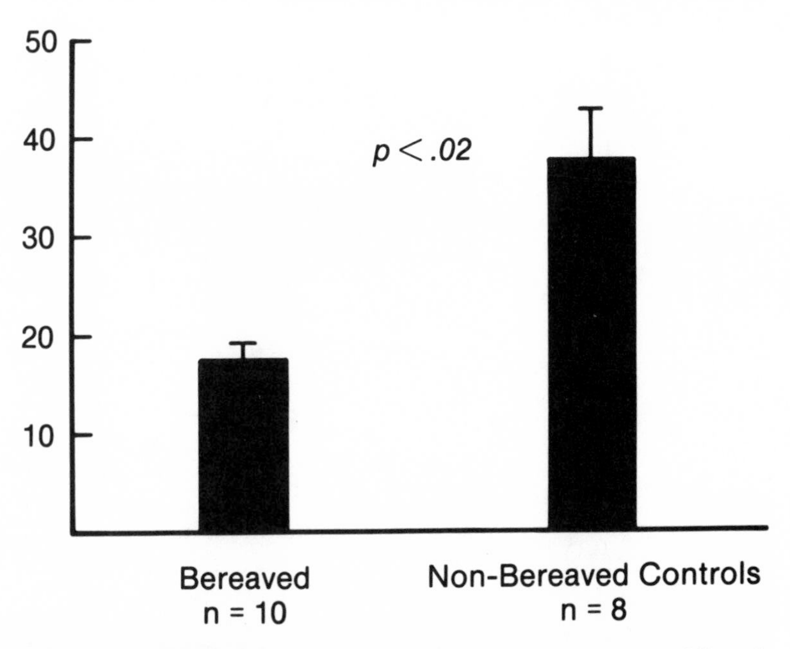

Figure 1. Natural killer cell activity in bereaved women (n = 10) and nonbereaved controls (n = 8). Range shown is group mean ± SE.

While the pattern of changes in immune function in this study is related to the intensity of depressive symptoms, the relative contribution of adverse life events and of depressive symptoms to changes in NK activity and the T helper to T suppressor cell ratio is difficult to determine from these data. However, the effects of depressive symptoms on immune function may be relatively more important than effects associated with life events. Changes in T cell subpopulations were related to depressive symptoms but not to group differences in the magnitude of life events. Locke and colleagues (44) have reported that lower cytotoxic activity is predicted by psychiatric symptoms but not by retrospective report of life change.

A Prospective Study of Depressive Symptoms and NK Activity

In a further study, we examined both NK activity and depressive symptoms one month before and after the death of a spouse in wives of men with incurable lung cancer. This prospective evaluation of six healthy women (mean age 57.3 years) permitted preliminary determination of whether impairment of NK activity is related to

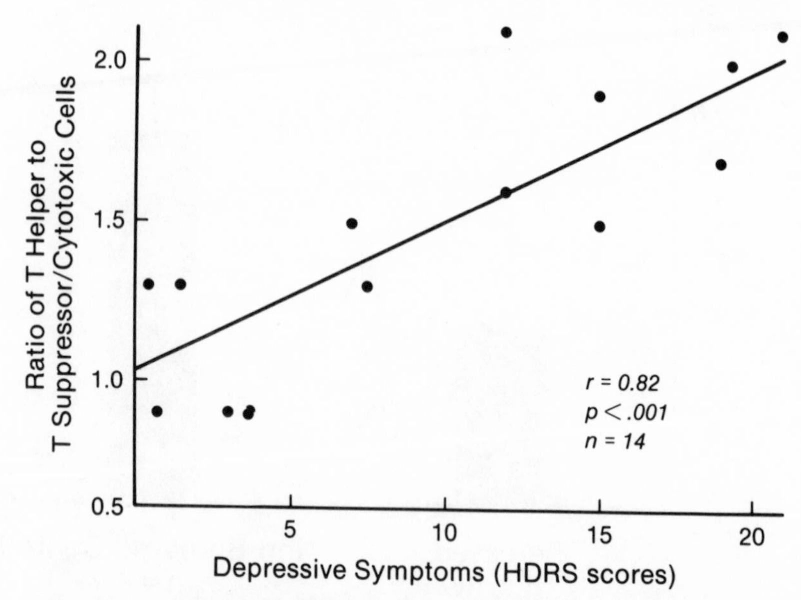

Figure 2. Relationship between ratio of T helper to T suppressor/cytotoxic cells and severity of depression symptoms. Each point represents the mean of multiple measures of the ratio of T helper to T suppressor cells in an individual subject.

the severity of depressive symptoms or is a consequence of the bereavement event.

Measures of NK activity were obtained at least twice in the pre- and the postbereavement periods and expressed as a mean for each subject to minimize the influence of immune measure variability. At prebereavement all subjects had moderately severe depressive symp-

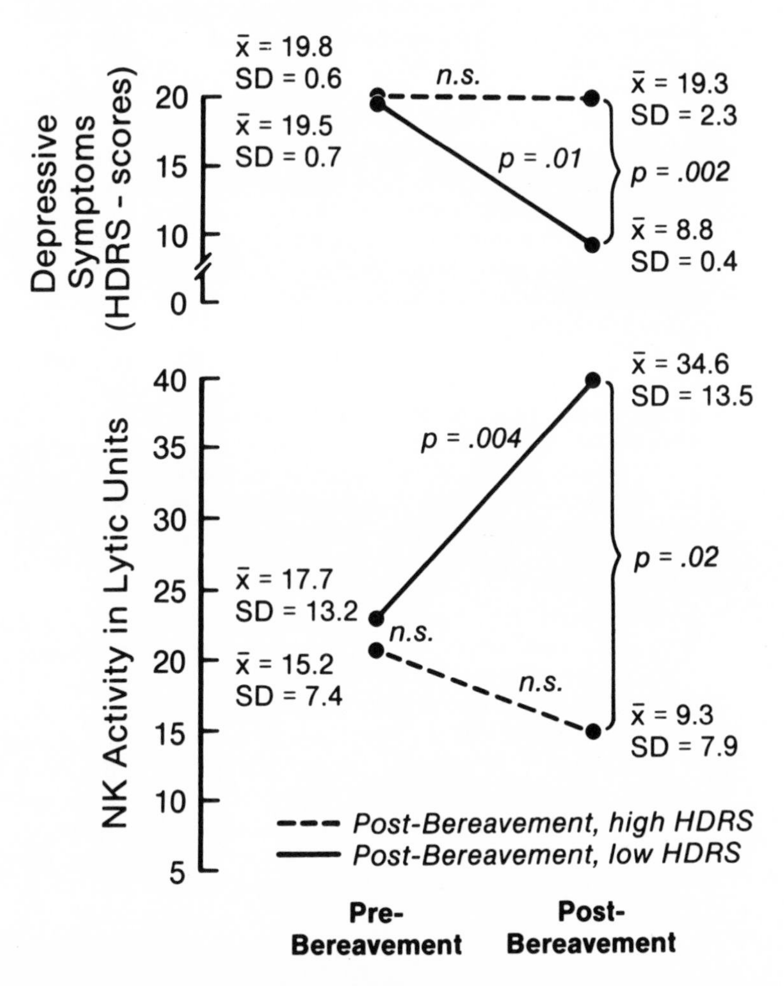

Figure 3. The pattern of change in depressive symptoms and natural killer cell activity during bereavement.

toms (HDRS scores $\geq$ 15). To test for the effects of depressive symptoms on immune function the subjects were divided into two groups based on the changes in severity of depressive symptoms (HDRS scores) from pre- to postbereavement.

Figure 3 provides these two group means ± SEMs for NK activity and HDRS scores at pre- and postbereavement periods and represents the pattern of these results. Though our series is admittedly small, results with these six cases demonstrate a significant time by post-bereavement HDRS interaction for NK activity and suggest that the resolution of depressive symptoms in women undergoing bereavement may be associated with a significant increase in NK activity. In contrast, other women demonstrate neither significant changes in depressive symptoms nor changes in NK activity from pre- to post-bereavement, and further, these women show an impairment of NK immune function at postbereavement as compared to women with few depressive symptoms. The death of the women's spouses does not seem to be associated with a consistent change in NK immune function (that is, there was no main effect of time on NK activity).

Our data strengthen the conclusions of other investigators that depressive and anxious symptoms are correlated with lower NK activity (42–44). In our study, subjects were longitudinally examined during severe, objective life changes and we did not rely on retrospective self-report; depressive symptoms were assessed using clinician observations; and variables that are known to affect immune function were controlled including health status, medication use, alcohol and tobacco use, and weight changes.

CONCLUSIONS

Several studies document an association between bereavement and both suppressed lymphocyte responses to mitogen stimulation and impaired NK activity. In addition, women who are bereaved and have depressive symptoms show alterations in T cell subpopulations including a relative loss of T suppressor/cytotoxic cells and an increase in the ratio of T helper to T suppressor/cytotoxic cells. While depressive symptoms may possibly mediate the immunologic changes during bereavement, the processes that modulate the immune system and link bereavement, changes in central nervous system activity, and immune function remain largely unexplored.

REFERENCES

1. Holmes TN, Rahe RH: The Social Readjustment Rating Scale. J Psychosom Res 11:213-218, 1967

2. Katz JL: Three studies in psychosomatic medicine revisited. Psychosom Med 44:29-42, 1982

3. Weiner H: The concept of stress in the light of studies on disasters, unemployment, and loss: a critical review, in Stress in Health and Disease. Edited by Zales MR. New York, Brunner/Mazel, 1984

4. Osterweis M, Solomon F, Green M (Eds): Bereavement reactions, consequences, and care. Washington, DC, National Academy Press, 1984

5. Jacobs S, Ostfeld A: An epidemiological review of the mortality of bereavement. Psychosom Med 39:344-357, 1977

6. Maddison D, Viola A: The health of widows in the year following bereavement. J Psychom Res 12:297, 1968

7. Parkes CM, Brown PJ: Health after bereavement. Psychosom Med 34:449-461, 1982

8. Mor V, McHorney C, Sherwood S: Secondary morbidity among the recently bereaved. Am J Psychiatry 143:158-163, 1986

9. Parkes CM: Recent bereavement as a cause of mental illness. Br J Psychiatry 110:198-204, 1984

10. Clayton PJ, Hirjanic M, Murphy GE: Mourning and depression: their similarities and differences. Can J Psychiatry 19:309-312, 1974.

11. Rees W, Lutkin SE: Mortality of bereavement. Br Med J 4:13-16, 1967

12. Parkes CM, Benjamin B, Fitzgerald RG: Broken heart: a statistical study of increased mortality among widowers. Br Med J 1:740, 1969

13. Young M, Benjamin B, Wallis C. Mortality of widowers. Lancet 2:454, 1963

14. Kraus AA, Lilienfield AM: Some epidemiological aspects of higher mortality rates in the widowed group. J Chronic Dis 10:207, 1959

15. Helsing KJ, Szklo M, Comstock EW: Factors associated with mortality after widowhood. Am J Public Health 71:802-809, 1981

16. Schmale AH: Relation of separation and depression to disease, I: a report on a hospitalized medical population. Psychosom Med 20:259-277, 1958

17. Engel GL: A life setting conducive to illness: the giving-up, given-up complex. Arch Intern Med 69:293-300, 1968

18. Shekelle RB, Raynor JW, Ostfeld AM, et al: Psychological depression and 12-year risk of death from cancer. Psychosom Med 43:117-125, 1981

19. Kerr TA, Schapiro K, Roth M: Relationship between premature death and affective disorders. Br J Psychiatry 115:1277-1282, 1969

20. Varsamis J, Zuchowski T, Main KK: Survival rate and causes of death in geriatric psychiatric patients. Canadian Psychiatric Association Journal 17:17-21, 1972

21. Whitlock FA, Siskind M: Depression and cancer: a follow-up study. Psychol Med 9:747-752, 1979

22. Niemi T, Jääskelainen J: Cancer morbidity in depressive persons. J Psychosom Res 22:117-120, 1978

23. Schleifer SJ, Keller SE, Camerino M, et al: Suppression of lymphocyte stimulation following bereavement. JAMA 250:374-377, 1983

24. Cohn M: What are the must elements of immune responsiveness?, in Neural Modulation of Immunity. Edited by Guillemin R, Cohn M, Melnechuk T. New York, Raven Press, 1985

25. Riley V: Psychoneuroendocrine influences on immunocompetence and neoplasia. Science 212:1100-1109, 1981

26. Hood LE, Weissman IL, Wood WB, et al (Eds): Immunology. Menlo Park, California, Benjamin-Cummings, 1985

27. Blumberg RS, Schooley RT: Lymphocyte markers and infectious diseases. Seminars in Hematology 22:31-114, 1985

28. Creemers PC, Stark DF, Boyko WJ: Evaluation of natural killer cell activity in patients with persistent generalized lymphadenopathy and acquired immunodeficiency syndrome. Clin Immunol Immunopathol 36:141-150, 1985

29. Schroff RW, Gottlieb MS, Prince HE, et al: Immunologic studies of homosexual men with immunodeficiency and kapos' sarcoma. Clin Immunol Immunopathol 27:300-314, 1983

30. Marx JL: How killer cells kill their targets. Science 231:1367-1369, 1986

31. Herberman RB, Ortaldo JR: Natural killer cells: their role in defenses against disease. Science 214:24-30, 1981

32. Makinodan R, Kay MMB: Age influences on the immune system. Adv Immunol 29:307, 1980

33. Smith HR, Steinberg AD: Autoimmunity—a perspective. Annual Review of Immunology 1:97-105, 1983

34. Bartrop RW, Lazarus L, Luckherst E, et al: Depressed lymphocyte function after bereavement. Lancet 1:834-836, 1977

35. Schleifer SJ, Keller SE, Stein M: Stress effects on immunity. Psychiatr J Univ Ottawa 10:125-131, 1956

36. Bloom ET, Babbitt JT: Monocyte mediated augmentation of human natural cell-mediated cytotoxicity. Cell Immunol 91:21-32, 1985

37. Bloom ET, Korn EL: Quantification of natural cytotoxicity by human lymphocyte subpopulations isolated by density: heterogeneity of the effector cells. J Immunol 58:323-335, 1983

38. Schleifer SJ, Keller SE, Meyerson AT, et al: Lymphocyte function in major depressive disorder. Arch Gen Psychiatry 41:484-486, 1984

39. Kronfol Z, House JD, Silva J, et al: Impaired lymphocyte function in depressive illness. Life Sci 33:241-247, 1983

40. Schleifer SJ, Keller SE, Siris SE, et al: Depression and immunity: lymphocyte function in ambulatory depressed hospitalized schizophrenic, and herniorrhaphy patients. Arch Gen Psychiatry 42:129-133, 1985

41. Schleifer SJ, Keller SE, Stein M, et al: Depression and lymphocyte function: role of age, sex, and severity. Annual Meeting of Biological Psychiatry, Washington, DC, May 7-11, 1986

42. Kiecolt-Glaser JK, Garner W, Speicher C, et al: Psychosocial modifiers of immunocompetence in medical students. Psychosom Med 46:7-14, 1984

43. Kiecolt-Glaser JK, Ricker D, Georg J, et al: Urinary cortisol levels, cellular immunocompetency, and loneliness in psychiatric inpatients. Psychosom Med 46:15-23, 1984

44. Locke SE, Kraus L, Leserman J, et al: Life change stress, psychiatric symptoms, and natural killer cell activity. Psychosom Med 46:441-453, 1984

45. Bistrian BR, Blackburn GL, Scrimshaw NS: Cellular immunity in semistarved status in hospitalized adults. Am J Psychol 28:1148-1155, 1975

46. Targan S, Britvan L, Dorey F: Activation of human NKCC molecular exercise. Clin Exp Immunol 45:352-360, 1981

47. Saxena QB, Megey E, Adler WH: Regulation of natural killer activity in vivo, II: The effect of alcohol consumption on human peripheral blood natural killer activity. Int J Cancer 26:413-417, 1980

48. Endicott J, Cohen J, Nee J, et al: Hamilton depression rating scale. Arch Gen Psychiatry 38:98-103, 1981

49. Shopsin B, Sathananthan GL, Chan TL, et al: Antinuclear factor in psychiatric patients. Biol Psychiatry 7:81-87, 1973

50. Deberbt R, Hooren JV, Biesbrouck M, et al: Antinuclear factor-positive mental depression: a single disease entity? Biol Psychiatry 11:69-74, 1976

51. Nemeroff CB, Simon JS, Haggerty JJ, et al: Antithyroid antibodies in depressed patients. Am J Psychiatry 142:840-843, 1985

52. Johnstone EC, Whaley K: Antinuclear antibodies in psychiatric illness: their relationship to diagnosis and drug treatment. Br Med J 28:724-725, 1975

Chapter 11

The Therapeutic Tasks of Grief

Stephen R. Shuchter, M.D.
Sidney Zisook, M.D.

Chapter 11

The Therapeutic Tasks of Grief

The most relevant aspect of the multidimensional model of spousal bereavement, discussed in Chapter 3, is that it provides a framework for the clinician to determine how to approach the treatment of problems that arise during bereavement. Rather than trying to establish the elusive definition of "pathological grief," the following "tasks" are used as operational definitions of the optimal outcome for each of the dimensions described:

1. Development of the capacity to experience, express, and integrate painful affects
2. Utilization of the most adaptive means of modulating painful affects
3. Integration of the continuing relationship with the dead spouse
4. Maintenance of health and continued functioning
5. Achievement of a successful reconfiguration of altered relationships
6. Achievement of an integrated, healthy self-concept and stable world view

Tasks 1 and 2: Development of the capacity to experience, express, and integrate painful affects; Utilization of the most adaptive means of modulating painful affects

These tasks are considered together because of the inevitable interactions between the two dimensions that they represent. The bereaved are repeatedly confronted by the competing forces of reality and psychological homeostasis. The former demands that they ex-

---

This chapter has been adapted from Shuchter SR: Dimensions of Grief: Adjustment to the Death of a Spouse, San Francisco, Jossey-Bass, 1986

perience the painful realization of their loss; the latter requires that they seek sanctuary from this painful realization.

Successful adaptation requires that the bereaved achieve a balance between the demands of reality and the safety provided by mechanisms which tend to obfuscate the reality. To be completely stripped of their defenses would lead to feeling overwhelmed and consumed by grief. To be too well defended could preclude dealing realistically with their loss. Thus, optimal balance occurs where the bereaved are able to feel their pain, loss, anger, and fear sufficiently to begin to integrate their experience, and yet have available to them a repertoire of protective (defensive) mechanisms to prevent them from being overwhelmed. While all of these coping mechanisms are primarily adaptive in their protective capacities, they are to be considered more adaptive and "healthy" to whatever degree they also serve other reality demands. While both working and compulsive eating may be protective through distraction or other gratification, clearly working is more likely to result in a useful product than eating. The tasks of a therapist in working with the bereaved would thus involve supporting those mechanisms which are secondarily more adaptive (for example, involvement with others, work, faith, and direct expression).

At the same time, the therapist must recognize the importance of timing and accessibility in helping the bereaved to "dose" the pain. The bereaved will instinctively move toward their protection. Unless they have a strong belief in the value of experiencing their anguish, it may be difficult for the therapist to maintain an arena in which to work with the emotions of the bereaved. Clearly, there are many survivors seeking an emotional outlet, and the therapist will have no difficulty in evoking such expression: The therapist's presence and availability alone will serve as vehicles to catharsis. For others, there is likely to be a significant resistance to such expression, and the therapist will need to counter these protective measures with both a cognitive rationale for the usefulness of catharsis as well as more powerful evocative techniques.

For some people, the "normalization" of many of their mental and emotional experiences can provide the permission to grieve more openly. Often, reading about someone else's similar experiences or empathizing with another widowed person's distress can provide the stimulus to grieve. One may not feel as alone or out of control when confronted by others' similar pain. What may not be permissible for oneself to experience can be sanctioned by another's suffering.

Use of specific evocative techniques for those who are experiencing absence of grief (1) or inhibited grief (2-4) have been described by many authors. At a practical level, these approaches all rely on reestablishing emotional links with perceptual experiences in order to elicit the painful experiences and expressions of grief. Verbal stimuli, visual imagery, and tangible reminders may be employed.

Verbal approaches may examine the circumstances of the spouse's death, reviewing the events in great detail, and looking for any evidence of an emotional response to be elaborated. The therapist may use language which is stronger, more expressive, and more evocative than the usually more neutral language of psychotherapy ("dead" rather than "lost;" "excruciating" rather than "difficult" or "painful").

A more powerful approach to eliciting affect employs the use of directed imagery. These techniques are directed at bringing the dead spouse into the emotional life of the bereaved, and knowledge of their relationship will give clues to the most useful approach. The therapist may help the bereaved reminisce about poignant times in their lives together, soliciting scenes in which the dead spouse plays a prominent role. Greater immediacy may be attained by bringing the dead spouse into the room through the use of role play. The therapist may ask the bereaved to try and visualize or pretend that the dead spouse is sitting in a chair, requesting that he or she speak to the spouse. Alternately, the bereaved may be asked to compose a letter to the dead spouse communicating what they have experienced or a sentiment which had gone unspoken. At times, the bereaved will be more capable of experiencing affect where it applies to others than to themselves, and the imagery might focus on the impact of the loss on their children.

The most powerful evocative stimuli are likely to be the tangible representations of the deceased, and the therapist can take advantage of this. Usually, the bereaved can identify those items for which they are most avoidant. Where this information is unavailable, the therapist can request that the person bring to a session a picture of the dead spouse alone or with the bereaved, an article of clothing or jewelry which has special meaning, old letters from the deceased, or other symbolic representations of the deceased.

For those who are most avoidant, the cemetery may be the stimulus which produces the greatest emotional response, and the therapist may encourage the bereaved to spend time at the grave, employing other techniques of reminiscing, communicating, and in other ways making efforts to bring the dead to life.

It should be remembered that the purpose of such techniques is to give the bereaved repetitive experiences with their grief and desensitize them to the pain. The goal is a gradual development of mastery. This does not mean "getting it out once and for all," but learning to tolerate the emotional pain so that the bereaved can have freer catharsis and can decrease the limitation which avoidance created in their emotional and day-to-day practical lives. Once the bereaved can think and speak more freely about the deceased, they will be more able to integrate the loss.

Task 3: Integration of the continuing relationship with the dead spouse

The process of integrating the loss of one's spouse psychologically involves a series of internal events beginning with the realization of the loss and culminating with acceptance of a physical and psychological reality.

The realization of loss is not simply an intellectual process, but is even more a reflection of the profound, deeply felt experiences of loss that are only achieved through recurrent painful encounters with the bereaved person's new reality.

While the concept of "acceptance" is one that would seem necessary to any definition of resolution or recovery, the question of what is being accepted becomes rather crucial. During the early weeks of grief, where the realization of loss has occurred with its accompanying painful emotions, the bereaved are usually in such a state of mental and emotional upheaval that questions of acceptance have rarely occurred to them. The loss seems rather raw, they feel relatively unprotected and overwhelmed much of the time. But what is acceptance? How does one accept the death of one's spouse? Is acceptance a resignation to live with something tragic, to embrace a disdainful reality, to agree that the death has happened? If that is the case, then, in fact, almost all of the bereaved can be said to have "accepted" their loss. But if "acceptance" means that the bereaved truly believe that the relationship with their spouse is *over, finished, completed* and that they are emotionally prepared to live with that, then it is the extraordinary person who achieves this kind of acceptance.

Freud (5) described the work of grief as enabling the bereaved to "decathect" the lost object. Bowlby (6), Parkes (7), and others have suggested that the grief reaction represents a specific, evolutionarily adaptive response whose primary purpose is to reunite the bereaved with the lost object. This latter view is consistent with the observations of Glick and Parkes (8) that continuing ties to the dead spouse appear consistently through the first year of bereavement. Data presented in this book and the work of others confirm the extension of such ties indefinitely over time. It is our contention that partial mitigation of the loss of a spouse through the continued emotional connection is both universal and essential, and that the task of the therapist is not to help the person "let go" or "give up" the relationship, but to help the bereaved find an appropriate place for the dead in their emotional lives which will enable them both to grieve and to continue living effectively in the world.

Psychologically, we are incapable of relinquishing all of the bonds, connections, and ties that are a part of our most intimate relationships. As a result, a revised definition of "acceptance" must include the notion that the bereaved person is emotionally prepared to live with an altered relationship with their dead spouse, sustained by ongoing contact and communication, dreams, memories, and living legacies. It is a mistake to expect that the death of a spouse means that the relationship is over, and a healthy adaptation to the death includes the evolution of a new form of this relationship and its integration into the changing life and personality of the bereaved.

The clinician's focus should be to facilitate and encourage the fullest expression of the grieving spouse's thoughts and feelings about the dead spouse. Recognizing the myriad forms which such continuing relationships can take, the therapist is in the position of eliciting information about areas where the bereaved may feel reluctant to disclose their experiences. Inquiry about their spouse's resting place; efforts to contact him or her; experiences of communication or "presences"; ongoing manifestations of symbolic representation and living legacies; rituals, memories, and dreams all serve to stimulate further thoughts and emotions that will promote further elaborations of such themes. The use here of normalization can overcome concerns that the bereaved may have about their "strangeness" in communicating with the dead or hallucinating their presence.

Most bereaved spouses find their own forms of communication and continuing contact with their dead spouses. Where there is too great an inhibition of expression of a phobic nature, employment of those techniques described earlier in this section may be necessary to desensitize the person and facilitate this process. Even after desensitization has occurred, the same evocative techniques—using directed imagery, role playing and reminiscing—can be useful tools in the ongoing therapeutic process.

Over time, traditional psychotherapeutic methods are employed to examine the spousal relationship as it existed before death, helping the bereaved achieve a realistic perspective about their marriage with its pluses and minuses, and about their spouse who may only have been human. The therapist must be patient, recognizing that ambivalence and angry feelings about one's spouse and marriage may be overshadowed by idealization in the early months after death. With "reworking" of the issues, the bereaved person moves through successive stages of understanding and enlightenment, and the ongoing relationship with their spouse proceeds to evolve. This process of integration occurs over many years and should be conveyed thus by the therapist.

Task 4: Maintenance of health and continued functioning

The increased risk among the newly bereaved for developing stress-related medical and psychiatric disorders is well documented but not well understood. Figure 1 depicts operational mechanisms, presumed here as a model, to determine dysfunction both on psychological and physiological bases.

Because of the increased medical morbidity, particularly during the first year of bereavement, the surviving spouse should have regular assessment by a primary care physician.

There is also a need for the clinician to address any issue which is likely to be contributing to stress beyond the primary stress produced by the loss. Among these may be financial difficulties created by loss of income, medical bills, or inadequate insurance. Legal and administrative problems relating to the disposition of an estate, filing for social security or veteran's benefits, complicated tax problems, or difficulties with decisions about where to live or how to invest may seem overwhelming to the newly bereaved. While the clinician may not have expertise in such areas, he or she can still be helpful

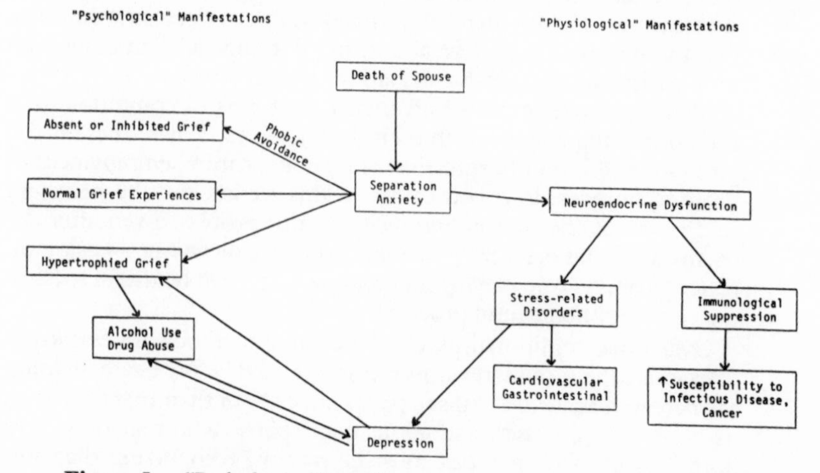

Figure 1. "Pathological" grief.

in different ways: 1) by helping the bereaved organize their thinking, by lending perspective to the problems, and by supporting efforts to confront anxiety-provoking situations; 2) by functioning as a resource directing the bereaved to appropriate experts in finance, law, and social resources; and 3) by acting as an advocate at times in obtaining temporary disability from work while a person is in a state of significant disorganization and confusion, or where a continuing psychiatric disturbance—particularly depression—subsequently develops.

While as many as one-half of the bereaved have some symptoms of depression during the first year after their spouses' deaths, estimates vary between 10 and 25 percent (9) as to who may develop significant clinical depression. While there have been no studies to demonstrate the efficacy of treating such depressions with antidepressants, there is no reason to presuppose that this treatment would not be beneficial, and our clinical experiences support this view. The major problem for the clinician involves the differentiation of those states which represent "real" depression from those "depressoid" states associated with grief. Both conditions share the symptoms of grief as well as depression. In those major depressions which occur during bereavement, there may be a significant elaboration of grief symptoms which are intensified by the depression. The two criteria that I have used in making this differentiation have been based primarily on features of the depression itself:

1. The depression has "a life of its own." The quality of having "a life of its own" refers to the persistence of depressive symptoms independent of the day-to-day events, the exposure to "triggers," or the internal psychological processes of the bereaved. These symptoms may worsen in response to such factors but they will continue when these factors are "neutral."
2. Vegetative signs and symptoms persist beyond two months after the death. Vegetative signs and symptoms of depression such as insomnia, anorexia with weight loss, depleted energy and easy fatigability, and psychomotor agitation may all be present as acute stress responses to the death of a spouse. Their persistence beyond the first two months is a strong indication that a clinical depression has evolved. Vegetative signs or symptoms which are less typical of acute stress reactions—hypersomnia, hyperphagia, and psychomotor retardation—are also suggestive of clinical depression.

The stance adopted here is that aggressive treatment of such clinical depression is important for two reasons. First, treatment of the depression is likely to lower the risk of medical sequelae to which the depressed are more vulnerable. Second, treatment of the depression will make the bereaved better able to cope with their grief. By limiting the dysfunction and intensified regression which are the usual consequences of depression, the bereaved will have more resources available to them to carry on with the tasks of life, as well as to allow the temporary and limited regressions forced upon them by their grief.

At a more speculative level, the argument has been presented (10) that antidepressants may have a place in the therapeutic armamentarium not just for treating the more clear-cut major depression associated with grief, but also for those cases of hypertrophied grief where its action may be primarily anxiolytic, lowering separation anxiety (see Figure 1).

At present, the place for anxiolytics and sedative-hypnotics has been and will likely continue to be based on the expressed intensity of need. Where the bereaved have identified a degree of suffering, particularly in the early weeks and months, which they are having great difficulty in tolerating—even where they have extended their full repertoire of defenses—there are few medical practitioners who would withhold what they feel is humane relief in the form of such medications. While such use is easier to sanction when it helps with sleep or limits the dysfunction that anxiety may wreak on performance, it takes a diehard believer in the usefulness of suffering to make a case for abstinence. The therapist should be working to help the bereaved find the most adaptive forms of alternately experiencing and containing their grief, but there are often periods when short-term and limited use of anxiolytics (and perhaps including low-dose antidepressants) may be necessary.

Alcoholism is another psychiatric disorder for which the bereaved are at great risk. The utility of small amounts of alcohol for sleep, diminishing anxiety, and obliterating ruminative thinking predispose the grieving survivor to find comfort in drinking, at times leading to gradual escalation and eventually to degrees of uncontrolled or obligatory consumption. At greatest risk are those bereaved who are recovering alcoholics or who have strong family histories of alcoholism. An essential component of any assessment is a careful and persistent inquiry about alcohol use and potential abuse. Where there is suspicion of alcoholism, vigorous pursuit of the question should extend to family and friends. Aggressive treatment is important to prevent the potentially severe consequences of alcoholism among the bereaved. Escalation of drinking frequently leads to an intensification of grief, precipitation of secondary depression, and greater impairment of function. Any efforts to treat alcoholism among the bereaved, regardless of one's therapeutic inclinations, should be done in conjunction with the person's involvement in Alcoholics Anonymous.

Alcoholism may also mask other disorders, particularly depressive or anxiety disorders, which have more specific, efficacious, and safer treatments. The person who is using more alcohol is likely to be rationalizing its use and denying its relevance so that ancillary information may be important.

The sense of entitlement "permits" the bereaved numerous indulgences besides alcohol which may be detrimental to their health: abuses of drugs, cigarettes, and food are all quite common. Aside from any ongoing supportive therapy which addresses issues specific to bereavement, addressing these special problems is probably best done in problem-specific treatment programs—for example, Overeaters Anonymous.

Task 5: Achievement of a successful reconfiguration of altered relationships

The therapeutic approach to problems which arise from the relationships of the bereaved is simple: figure out what's wrong and help to fix it. Beyond this general principle, the clinician is faced with innumerable possibilities where difficulties can arise for the bereaved, each having idiosyncratic dynamics and a wide variety of potential solutions. What is important for the clinician is a knowledge of the normal and usual variants and an appreciation for unusual aspects of grief that may need special handling. Otherwise these problems are treated using supportive and exploratory psychotherapeutic approaches to intrapsychic and relationship problems as well as family therapy, couples therapy, and even consultation with other individuals with whom conflicts may arise.

Normalization through education can be quite useful in helping the bereaved to appreciate the universality of many of the relationship problems that can occur. This can combat some of the demoralization that arises from seeing others express their fears of grief through criticism or rejection of the bereaved. Education of family and friends through reading or consultation may yield enormous benefits where greater understanding of the plight of the bereaved emerges.

Confronting the fear and inhibitions about developing new friendships and possible romantic relationships usually involves exploration of the impact of their loss, as well as support and encouragement to pursue these relationships. The therapist and the bereaved may discover "developmental arrests" of certain social skills which were subsumed by the marriage and which require "exercise" to be revitalized.

Changing social customs with greater sexual openness, freedom, and demands may deter some from social reentry until they feel more secure about their own beliefs. Examining and overcoming guilt may be prerequisites to experiencing any social pleasures and is more conflictual when dating, sexuality, and remarriage are concerned. The therapist can help the bereaved to acknowledge their continuing ties to their spouse, and to reassure them of the emotional reality that this does not preclude other simultaneous relationships. Over time, such gentle suggestions may free up the bereaved sufficiently to "try on" other relationships.

Task 6: Achievement of an integrated, healthy self-concept and stable world view

There are several important contributions that the therapist can make in helping the bereaved to deal with their changing identity and belief systems. Initially, a crucial precondition to offering help is a thorough understanding of this dimension of grief. The therapist must recognize the early regression for what it is and communicate it as such to the bereaved. The therapist must also be able to maintain a conviction about the bereaved person's adaptive capacities, a feat made difficult by the strong regressive pull on the therapist of the grieving person's feelings of helplessness, hopelessness, and inadequacy. The intensity and power of such feelings cannot be underestimated and the therapist's exposure to these affects may not be duplicated in many other clinical situations. Communicating this knowledge and conviction to the bereaved is a difficult task, but this therapeutic stance may need to be sustained over an extended period of time in order to provide the support necessary to prevent further demoralization in the bereaved.

Where the bereaved find their lives meaningless or directionless, they will seek direction and advice from the therapist. While clinicians may have different views of what constitute adaptive directions, the most supportive stance is usually to communicate repeatedly that the bereaved will be quite capable of making decisions or taking actions which will affect themselves at a time when they are "ready," and that until that time they should probably defer any decisions or actions that are not essential. During this period of time, the bereaved are likely to be operating almost solely on the principle of "what hurts least is best," and impulsive actions designed to anticipate relief of pain are likely to occur. At such times, the bereaved may require greater degrees of support and more active direction by the therapist toward safety or the prevention of irreversible actions such as changing jobs or selling homes.

As the bereaved emerge from the period of greatest regression, the changes in identity, personal growth, and attitudinal shifts generally proceed spontaneously and effectively. The therapist then becomes more of a mirror reflecting such changes and supporting those behaviors which will promote further growth through the bereaved person's excursions into new relationships, new careers, and new ways of thinking about the world and themselves. This mirror should be "real," demonstrating the therapist's genuine joy, pride, and enthusiasm for the growth that is evident.

The force that enables the therapist to accomplish many of these tasks is a powerful positive transference which is derived from the intensified object-hunger of the bereaved, and which is further promoted by the therapist's willingness to serve as a transitional object during this period. The emotional demands upon the therapist are great. The need to empathize with such powerful painful emotions creates a challenge for the most experienced therapists, and therapists need to be aware of their own internal forces seeking relief from feelings of being overwhelmed. Another prevalent countertransference response is the fear of being "devoured" by the intense needs of the bereaved. Therapists must recognize the temporary nature of such regression and not "run" from it.

Support Groups for the Bereaved

The Widow-to-Widow program developed by Silverman (11, 12) in the late 1960s has evolved into the prototype for mutual support groups in this country and in Great Britain, and this model has been adopted subsequently by the American Association of Retired Persons in establishing its Widowed Person's Service with branches throughout this country. The efficacy of such support groups has been established in several studies (13, 14), and these programs provide continuing support services for the bereaved as a significant public health intervention strategy.

The benefits of such an organization are multiple. For a great number of the bereaved, their participation in the small groups is felt to be their only access to people who they feel can understand them or where their feelings are acceptable, thus providing them with their only means of catharsis. The universality of their experiences provides great reassurance that they are not "going crazy" and that others have gone through the same things and have come out not only intact but often stronger. At the same time, the uniqueness of their losses is respected and supported and they are made to feel important. The bonds that develop among people are very strong as they join a club whose "dues" are high, and as they offer each other their mutual support. Much practical information is shared, which may make day-to-day living easier: some participants have developed know-how in dealing with social security and veteran's benefits, and others in finding a trustworthy auto mechanic. Organized social and recreational activities with a growing extended family can help to structure a life that may seem relatively empty. Exercising one's social skills occurs more easily in an atmosphere of support without the sexual demands that are experienced in other settings. Yet to be determined is the relative therapeutic efficacy of support groups in contrast to individual therapy for the bereaved. Clearly there is considerable overlap in their functions in dealing with most of the dimensions of grief.

REFERENCES

1. Deutsch H: Absence of grief. Psychoanal 6:12-22, 1937
2. Volkan VD: "Re-grief" therapy, in Bereavement: Its Psychological Aspects. Edited by Schoenberg B, Gerber I. New York, Columbia University Press, 1975
3. Mawson D, Marks IM, Ramm L, et al: Guided mourning for morbid grief: a controlled study. Psychiatry 138:185-193, 1981
4. Melges FT, DeMaso DR: Grief resolution therapy: reliving, revising, and revisiting. Am J Psychother 34:51-70, 1980
5. Freud S: Mourning and Melancholia (1917), in Complete Psychological Works, Standard Edition, vol. 14. Translated and edited by Strachey J. London, Hogarth Press, 1961
6. Bowlby J: Attachment and Loss, vol. III. New York, Basic Books, 1980
7. Parkes CM: Bereavement. London, Tavistock, 1972
8. Glick IO, Parkes CM, Weiss R: The First Year of Bereavement. New York, Basic Books, 1975
9. Osterweis M, Solomon F, Green M (Eds): Bereavement: Reactions, Consequences, and Care. Washington, DC, National Academy Press, 1984
10. Shuchter SR: Antidepressant treatment of grief reactions, in Scientific Proceedings of the 135th Annual Meeting of the American Psychiatric Association, Toronto, Canada, May 15–21, 1982
11. Silverman PR: The Widow-to-Widow program: an experiment in preventive intervention. Mental Hygiene 53:333-37, 1969
12. Silverman PR, MacKenzie D, Pettipas M, et al (Eds): Helping Each Other in Widowhood. New York, Health Sciences Publishing, 1974
13. Vachon MLS, Sheldon AR, Llancee WJ, et al: A controlled study of self-help intervention for widows. Am J Psychiatry 137:1380-1384, 1980
14. Videka-Sherman L: Effects of participation in a self-help group for bereaved parents: Compassionate Friends. Prevention in Human Services 1:69-77, 1982